# BUDDHIST YOGA

# BUDDHIST
# YOGA

*by Rev. Kanjitsu Iijima*

Japan Publications, Inc.

©1975 BY JAPAN PUBLICATIONS, INC.

*Original edition published in Japanese by Japan Publications, Inc., Tokyo, in 1973.*

*Published by*
JAPAN PUBLICATIONS, INC., Tokyo, Japan

*Distributed by*
JAPAN PUBLICATIONS TRADING COMPANY
200 Clearbrook Road, Elmsford, N.Y. 10523, U.S.A.
1255 Howard Street, San Francisco, Calif. 94103, U.S.A.
P.O. Box. 5030 Tokyo International, Tokyo 101–31, Japan

First edition: May 1975
*ISBN 0–87040–349–4*
Printed in Japan by Kyodo Printing Co., Ltd.

# Foreword

Yoga and Buddhism constitute the zenith of Oriental culture. The Orient can therefore make its greatest contribution to mankind through Buddhism and Yoga. But the books on Buddhism and Yoga now being distributed throughout the world contain many misinterpretations and often suggest that the part may be taken for the whole. This is most regrettable.

Documented Yoga is approximately three thousand years old, and Buddhism has a history of some two thousand five hundred years. To date, the founder of Buddhism, Shakyamuni Buddha, is the "supreme practitioner of Yoga" in human history. Buddha is, in other words, a saint who brought the Yoga way to perfection. Consequently, if anyone teaching Yoga has not yet entered Buddhism, his theory can only be called immature. The present book, on the contrary, is a mature work. In this sense I wholeheartedly recommend to all people this book by Rev. Iijima.

The world today is in a turmoil of confusion and distress. Science has advanced so far that we can fly to the moon, but it has not made man happier. There is an increase in the numbers of the mentally ill, and the tragedies of war continue almost unabated. Serious diseases are spreading, crimes are becoming more brutal, broken homes are commonplace, and the fear of traffic accidents is mounting. Religious people, politicians, and physicians are all looking for a way out, but no practical solution has been found. This is the situation. Into this situation Yoga and Buddhism come with a certain inevitability.

The saying "Light comes from the East" is ancient. But today, more than ever, man needs this "Light from the East." Only in Yoga and Buddhism can men find solutions to the many difficult problems that presently confront them. Yet people who do not know Yoga or Buddhism will doubtless have misgivings about this affirmation. Rev. Iijima's book is admirably suited to answering people's questions and resolving such misgivings. With all the fervor I can command, I urge everyone to read this book.

The relationship between Rev. Iijima and myself goes back many years. He studied at a Buddhist university and a Christian theological school, but he credits me with opening his eyes to Yoga and being his teacher. He has already published numerous works on Buddhism and Christianity, and I am sure he will continue to write about Yoga and Buddhism for the sake of world peace. I consider him one of the most gifted and sincere religious leaders of this century and earnestly desire that readers of his book may be led to the gate of enlightenment and salvation.

MASAHIRO OKI

*Yoga Hall*
*777 Sawachi, Mishima-shi*
*Shizuoka-ken, Japan*

# Preface to the Japanese Edition

This book was written in the hope that religious leaders and physicians all over the world will read it. The reason I entertain this hope is that after forty years of study and experience, I have reached the conclusion that religion and medical science must become one.

Man's mind and body are no more separable than the front and back of a sheet of paper. If the body weakens, the mind is certain to weaken, and conversely, when the mind weakens, the body too becomes weak. In spite of the efforts of religious leaders, man does not show much improvement in mind or spirit; and despite the efforts of physicians, the number of sick people does not decrease. This is because neither religious leaders nor doctors understand precisely the connection between man's mind and body. Even if a religious leader cures a man's spirit, if bad physical habits are not corrected, they will cause the mind to deteriorate just as ink absorbed by a blotter penetrates all the way through. Similarly, even if a doctor cures a man's illness, unless bad mental habits are corrected, they will affect the body and the illness will return. For a religious leader to try to improve a man's mind without taking account of his body, or for a doctor to cure an illness without taking note of the patient's mental condition, is as foolish as increasing the number of fire engines without trying to eliminate the causes of fires.

Man is man, not merely a body and not merely a mind. Just as it is impossible to find a sheet of paper with a front and no back or a back and no front, so a mind-only man or a body-only man does not exist anywhere in this world. But, mirabile dictu, there do exist signs advertising cures for the body apart from the mind, and for the mind apart from the body. How strange it would be to see signs announcing the sale of the front of a sheet of paper without the back!

The body and mind are the two wings of a bird. If one wing is damaged, no amount of effort with the other wing will enable the bird to fly. One must not jump to the conclusion that if a bird can fly ten miles with two wings, he can fly five miles with one. Only when both wings work simultaneously and harmoniously can the bird fly.

To this relationship, characterized by simultaneity and complementarity, I have given the name "multiplication principle," for man's mind and body do in fact depend on this principle. Doctors and religious leaders who are aware of this interrelation often say, "The body and mind are very closely connected with each other, so to cure the one, the other must be taken into consideration as well." We need to realize, however, that the body-mind relationship is not a "very close connection" but an "inseparable oneness." It is like the relationship between male and female—not "very close" but "inseparable." The male does not exist for the sake of the female, nor the female for the male. In the same way, one must not say he will use the mind for the sake of the body, nor the body to benefit the mind. From the beginning, mind and body constitute "one person," not a "relationship." The yogi of ancient India grasped this important principle, and Gautama or Shakyamuni the Buddha brought it to completion. This I call "the way of body and mind."

Buddhism was, at the outset, a "Way of the unity of body and mind." But many past masters failed to understand this and took it to be simply a "Way of the mind" like religions in general. I believe this is the main reason for the stagnation of contemporary Buddhism, the main reason it is presently unable to make a significant contribution to the welfare of mankind.

This book was written in the desire to correct this misapprehension and to restore the original Buddhist "Way of body and mind." The Japanese title of this Book, *Bukkyō yōga nyūmon* [Introduction to Buddhist Yoga], illustrates this intention. To dispel the common illusion suggested by the word "Buddhism," that it is a "Way of the mind," I added the word "Yoga" to indicate that it is a "Way of body and mind."

This book is nothing more than an introduction to the subject, but I firmly believe it will suggest new solutions to the problems and sufferings people experience in today's world. Family problems, sufferings caused by sickness and disease, problems relating to one's work and, on a broader scale, problems in the sphere of politics, society, and world peace—this book proposes the basic principles for their solution. Into the shaping of these principles have gone forty years of sutra study, 10,000 sermons, 20,000 cold water austerities, and 25,000 pages of manuscript.

I am blessed with five children, and while writing this book, I could not suppress the feeling that it was to be my last will and testament to them. I have published several books before this one, but they were presented in a form accommodated to the capacities of the readers instead of explaining the principles in and of themselves. This book, however, goes to the heart of the matter. As such, it is a lasting gift to my children, and in bringing it to completion I feel I have accomplished part of my obligation as a father.

That a mere seeker after truth like myself has been able to come this far is due to the guidance of many masters. By inscribing their names here I hope to express a token of my profound gratitude. They are:

The Reverend Nisshō Honda  
The Reverend Masaharu Taniguchi  
The Reverend Entai Tomomatsu  

Dr. Katsuo Nishi  
Dr. Taka'aki Ōhura  
Dr. Masahiro Oki  

Also, to Mrs. Ellen Granstedt, Mrs. Tsuru Masuhara, and Mr. and Mrs. Fusao Hori, who provided me with both tangible and intangible support during the period of writing, I wish to express in the name of the Buddha my heartfelt appreciation. Finally, to Mrs. Kaori Takagi, Mr. Namio Gotō, Miss Miyoko Kojiri, and Miss Hisako Oshiba of Dr. Oki's Yoga Hall, all of whom gave willingly of their time and talent to make possible the photographs that appear in this book, I wish to acknowledge their overwhelming support and helpfulness, far beyond the call of duty, and extend to them this word of sincere thankfulness.

KANJITSU IIJIMA

*Dharma Yoga Church Institute*  
*Los Angeles, California*

# Preface to the American Edition

Quite some time has passed since people began to talk about the "crisis of Christianity" in America. Yet despite the unflagging diligence of countless religious leaders, the crisis continues. Children from broken homes wander the streets like orphans, and drug addiction has spread even to the young in our junior high schools. Windows are boarded up because of rampant crime, thus creating a "dead city" within the urban sprawl. In the strictest sense one can no longer speak of America as a Christian nation or even as a land of law and order.

I do not believe Christianity has lost the ability to help people of this century. It is not an anachronism simply because its essence is "a thing of the past." The spirit of Jesus Christ is such that it will shine radiantly as a sublime treasure so long as man continues on this earth. The question is: how can the "God" Jesus embraced be brought to the hearts of today's people?

The Bible describes Jesus' "method of communication" in these words:

> With many such parables he would give them his message, so far as they were able to receive it. He never spoke to them except in parables; but privately to his disciples he explained everything (Mark 4:33–34).

As indicated in this passage, Jesus adapted his method of communication to the capacities and situations of his hearers. Here brushing the surface, there going to the depths, now in brief, now in detail—all sorts of means were used to lead men to God. Consequently, anyone who insists that nothing should be taught except what is in the Bible, or that what cannot be found in the Bible should not be taught, is going against the true intent of Jesus.

The men and women of this century possess twentieth-century minds. Anyone can fly around the world in a day— a feat that would have been inconceivable to people of the first century. Since those ancient days, man's way of thinking and character have undergone fundamental changes. As a result, teachings intended to lead men to God must also be changed in such a way as to be understandable and acceptable to men of this century. Is this not what is meant by "practicing the love of God" and "being faithful to Jesus"?

There are doubtless many reasons why twentieth-century men and women, including religious leaders, find it difficult to maintain a living faith in God, but two factors are of particular importance. First, with the rise of modern science and the prestige attaching to everything scientific, people have developed the habit of not being able to believe anything that has not first been proved intellectually. Second, because the physical environment has become so unnatural, the brain has become abnormal with the result that people have to a great extent lost the instinctive power to feel the real existence of God. In order to lead people of this century to God, therefore, two conditions must be met. The existence of God must be proven intellectually, and the physical environment must be brought back into harmony with nature.

Throughout our long history, it has often been said that an intellectual verification of God is impossible. But is it really so? For ages it was also said that man could not fly through the air since he is not a bird. But as a result of the efforts of modern men, this myth has been stood on its head. The legend that an intellectual verification of the existence of God is impossible is also about to be overturned. This verification is given in my "theory of the dharma."

Weakened instinctive power, moreover, can definitely be regained by all people through the practice of a method intended to reform body and brain. This is the "theory of Yoga" I have taught for many years.

Neither the dharma nor Yoga are my discoveries. They are both "truths" discovered over twenty-five hundred years ago—but in recent years nearly forgotten.

This book is nothing but an introduction to the subject, so the explanations found here will not be entirely adequate. But I am convinced that anyone who grasps the truth of this book will find, if he is a man of faith, that his faith in God will be strengthened or, if he is an atheist, that he will gain a new appreciation of the value of religion.

The oneness constituted by Yoga and Buddhism is not a "religion" in the usual sense of the word. It is "truth," so one who studies this truth from the standpoint of faith will find his faith confirmed. Jesus said, "You shall know the truth, and the truth will set you free" (John 8:32). Neither Yoga nor Buddhism call for "conversion." Their only desire is that one who studies the truth will find his faith enriched.

America! Call to mind the motto engraved on your coins: "In God we trust." That this book may be of some help in leading people to trust in God anew is the fervent wish of the author in presenting this book to the people of America.

Kanjitsu Iijima

*Dharma Yoga Church Institute*
*Los Angeles, California*

# Contents

# 1. Foundation for the Way of Body and Mind

# The Buddha

## THE NAME "SHAKYAMUNI BUDDHA"

The tallest mountains in the world, the Himalayas, are located on the northern border of India. The subcontinent is a land of merciless heat, but the peaks of the Himalayas are snowcapped the year round. On their slopes, in an area now called Nepal, Shakyamuni Buddha was born and raised.

The personal name of this remarkable man was Siddhartha and his family name Gautama. After he attained enlightenment at the age of thirty-five, he was also designated by the titles "Muni" and "Buddha." The formal and most respectful way of speaking of him was to append these titles to the name of his clan, "Shakya," thus arriving at the name "Shakyamuni Buddha."

"Muni" means "holy sage" or one who has achieved the highest state. "Buddha" means "awakened one" or one who has had his eyes opened and attained the highest wisdom. Both terms existed long before Siddhartha's time, but no one before or since seems to have been truly worthy of these honorary titles. To this day, no one is called "Muni" or "Buddha" except Shakyamuni Buddha.

The scriptures of Buddhism comprise some ten thousand volumes. Both in the Agama, generally regarded as the scriptures of primitive Buddhism, and in the subsequently developed scriptures of Mahayana Buddhism, Siddhartha is consistently referred to as "Shakyamuni Buddha." It is never shortened to "Shakya Buddha" or "Shakyamuni," but is always "Shakyamuni Buddha." This usage can hardly be coincidental, and it suggests that a deep meaning was intended.

## SIDDHARTHA THE TRUTH-SEEKER

Prince Siddhartha, as the crown prince, was given the best education and training possible, but he was dissatisfied with palace life. He was also a family man, blessed with a kind father, King Shuddhodana, a beautiful wife, Princess Yashodhara, and a son, Rahula. But on his twenty-ninth birthday, during the middle of the night, he left the palace and became an itinerant truth-seeker. He took a path south, descended the Himalayas, crossed the Ganges River, and wandering from this hill to that, this forest to that, he earnestly sought good teachers.

At the time of his quest, the religions of India had reached an amazing state of development. This can be ascertained by reading the religious texts of that period, the Vedas and Upanishads, both of which still exist today. Such reading will show that in the India of that day religions of all kinds, with a great variety of religious ideas drawn from many ages and nations, were blooming in full glory like a multitude of flowers. Siddhartha eagerly absorbed all of them. For the purpose of explanation, these religions can be classified in three groups.

The first was a traditional form of religion that began about a thousand years before Buddha's time. It was based on the Vedas and its priests were called Brahmans. The second was a cluster of "new" religious movements described in the Upanishads. They arose in opposition to the formalism of Brahmanism and advocated a philosophical ideology uniquely their own. Their teachers were called Shramana. The third was a group that already possessed a history of some five hundred years. It was based mainly on the practice of Yoga, and its teachers were called yogi. They did not recognize any scripture as authoritative and endeavored to attain a state of salvation primarily through physical austerities.

Siddhartha had already studied the traditional religion while he was yet a youth, for outstanding Brahmans were called to the palace to instruct him. But he could not find satisfaction in their formalistic approach. So when he became a wandering seeker after truth, for the most part he sought out dedicated men of the opposition movements and Yoga. Being a man of inherently great intelligence, Siddhartha had no particular difficulty comprehending the philosophy of the protest movements. But Yoga confronted him with a different kind of problem. Yoga was not something to be understood intellectually or intuitively. It required engaging the whole body. It is readily understandable, therefore, that the six years of his existence as a truth-seeker have become known in legend as his "six years of ascetic suffering."

In the sutra known as the *Majjhima Nikaya* it is written:

> His arms and legs looked like withered reeds, his buttocks like a camel's back; his spine protruded like a coarse rope, his ribs like the eaves of an ancient, rotting house. His scalp was as furrowed as an unripened gourd exposed to the sun. Only his eyes sparkled like a star sheltered at the bottom of a deep well. If he pressed his stomach, he could grasp his spine, and if he passed his hand over his vertebrae, he could take hold of the skin of his abdomen. When he tried to stand, he staggered and fell; his hair, rotted out at the roots, fluttered down. The crown prince thought, "Of all the ascetics and priests of ages past, or future, none has undergone to such an extreme the sufferings I have experienced."

One type of picture illustrating this period of asceticism shows a gaunt and emaciated Siddhartha fasting in seated meditation. Another shows a bird making a nest atop the head of the meditating Shakya—and staying there until its eggs hatch. Such a tale may not be factual, but what an excellent evocation of the actual asceticism of Buddha!

These six years involved more than ascetic practices. Siddhartha spent this time studying the Brahman way, which was based on faith, the Shramana way, which was essentially one of contemplation, and the Yoga way, which centered in physcial practices. Why, then, is this period of his life known as the legendary "six years of ascetic suffering"? Because neither faith nor contemplation, no matter how intense, manifest themselves externally, whereas Yoga austerities, being directly connected to the physical body, led to results visible to all eves.

## TRUE MEANING OF ASCETIC PRACTICE

The methods and varieties of ascetic practices are countless. But a study of the Buddhist scriptures for the purpose of determining the kinds of ascetic practices undertaken by Buddha suggests that they may be classified under four headings.

First came the breathing austerity. In this exercise one would prolong the breathing process, hold the breath, and learn abdominal breathing. The second was austerity in eating. One meal a day was the norm, but at times one would fast for several weeks. Third was the austerity of disciplining the skin. This involved enduring the cold without the protection of clothes, submerging oneself in water for days on end, and exposing oneself to the burning sun for hours. The fourth involved exercises for the disciplining of the body through standing for hours on one leg, or hanging upside down with both legs hooked over a branch, or twisting the torso into extreme positions. The Yoga practiced in present-day India can also be divided into these four variations.

What made such practices necessary? They were means to the healthy body and clear brain one had to have for ascetic training. If one had a cold, he could not train well. If his mind was dull from lack of sleep, his ability to think clearly would be affected. This is the kind of reasoning that led to the need for Yoga as a method of strengthening body and mind. The ultimate purpose was to enter into a state of absolute freedom, to realize godliness. Yoga was not, therefore, a way to physical health pure and simple. It also involved attaining the correct inner attitude. As such, it was "a health method for attaining godliness."

The phrase "health method," however, had a deeper meaning in ancient India than it has today. The greater profundity of the term in ancient usage appears in at least seven respects. As opposed to the comparatively shallow meaning of the term today, in times past it meant: health that entails not only strengthening of the body but making the brain clear and sharp; health which produces not merely a sturdy looking body but gives endurance and power; health that increases one's ability to adjust to changes in his surroundings; health that sharpens the senses; health that heightens one's ability to defend himself against enemies; health that issues in tender emotions; and health that brings forth a strong will.

It is said that both the American astronauts and Soviet cosmonauts underwent Yoga training. This is perfectly understandable, for to them enduring, indestructible health is a must. The Yoga practitioners of ancient India must have plunged themselves into ascetic practice with much the same kind of feeling that possesses today's explorers of outer space. From this point of view, it is readily understandable that in both cases the training program should become more and more rigorous.

Even in learning to play golf, one finds that surprising things happen. One friend, notorious for always sleeping late, decided by some turn of fortune to take up golf. Till that time, he could never get out of bed before 9 A.M., but soon he started to arise at 7, then 6, and now he rolls out at 4 A.M. to head for the golf course. He is himself mystified by this change. An outsider, seeing him get up so early, might describe his behavior as ascetic. Ascetic practice simply means exerting oneself, but to a non-participant, it appears as troublesome exertion, and that is how asceticism got its name. It is often associated with "excess," but of course overdoing is possible in any sphere.

"Every Sunday, my husband spends the entire day at the golf course without any regard for the children. What can I do?" The golf widow's complaint is a common one. Yoga practitioners are also only human, so it is only natural that some carry their austerities too far. Then too, some people go into Yoga from wrong motives. Just as a circus performer may practice difficult stunts to display to an audience, so too a person practicing Yoga may occasionally go to extremes just to show off. Buddha's practice was altogether different. His intelligence was too keen to allow him to become an extremist, and his position in life was such that he had no need to seek plaudits.

Why, then, did he undergo austerities so excruciating that he was led to say, "Of all the ascetics and priests of ages past, present, or future, none has undergone to such an extreme the sufferings I have experienced"? To answer this question is one of the motives for this book.

## BUDDHA AS A MASTER OF KENPŌ

Shakyamuni studied, then, each and every religion in the India of his day, but still he was not satisfied. The six years of itinerant truth-seeking, however, were not spent in vain. On the contrary, it is because of those six years of incomparably rigorous austerities that he was able, in my opinion, to attain the Great Enlightenment that came to him beneath the bodhi tree. Without the ascetic practices, the crown prince would have remained a crown prince forever. He would never have become Buddha. The last stone that capped the pyramid could be put in place only because of the painstaking labor that had erected the structure from the ground up. In this sense his attainment of enlightenment was a consequence not only of the six years immediately preceding this experience but also of his inborn character, his surroundings, his experiences as a prince, and the hedonistic palace life which stood almost as a polar opposite to the extremes of the six years of suffering.

Besides his mastery of scholarly knowledge, special note must be made of the fact that Shakyamuni also appears to have made himself a master of the martial arts. Since Siddhartha was born a crown prince during a turbulent period of civil wars, it was only natural that he would have received extensive training in the military arts. It is written in the sutra known as the *Lalita Vistara* that in *kenpō* (something like karate), archery, and all the martial arts, Shakyamuni had no equal. Yet when still a small boy, he was deeply distressed at the sight of a worm caught in a bird's beak. What contrasts existed in this man!

Buddha died at Kushinagara, the capital of Malla in central India. It is said that the eight pallbearers at his funeral were *kenpō* experts of Malla. The *kenpō* master Shakyamuni must have been held in deep respect by the Malla followers of *kenpō*.

About A.D. 500 the renowned sage Bodhidharma (often abbreviated "Dharma") journeyed from southern India to northern China as a Buddhist missionary. While in China he stayed at a temple (no longer extant) named Shao-lin-ssŭ. He was filled with the conviction that he was capable of communicating correctly the teachings of the Buddha himself. Dharma's teachings had two aspects: "the practice of meditation" and "the practice of muscle control." The word "meditation" needs no explanation. The word "muscle" as used in this context means the tendon, a cord-like connective tissue that joins one bone to another. What Dharma meant by "muscle control" is, therefore, very close to what we mean today by physical exercise. Yet what he had in mind was not exercise alone but something close to *kenpō*. That Dharma, who considered himself a direct disciple of Buddha, taught *kenpō* along with meditation is a point of considerable significance. Because of the teacher, this disciple existed. This too suggests that Shakyamuni Buddha was a master of *kenpō*.

## MUNI'S ATTAINMENT OF BUDDHAHOOD

Even though Shakyamuni became Buddha because he was gifted in all respects, including innate abilities and a propitious environment, this should not lead one to imagine that "the ascetic practices were a waste of effort." I find it most regrettable that a number of first-rate Buddhist scholars of past and present proclaim that these six years served no useful purpose whatever. How could Buddha, possessor of an intelligence without peer, spend six years of his life fruitlessly? The suggestion to be made here is that the phrase "useless ascetic practices" be understood to mean that he "graduated from ascetic practices."

There could have been no regrets in the heart of Prince Siddhartha as he washed away in the Nairañjanā river the grime of six years of truth-seeking. There was no need now to seek out a teacher or undertake more ascetic practices. He may well have had a premonition that he was about to attain buddhahood. After six years of pilgrimage, no, from the day of his birth till now, throughout a life marked by every conceivable sort of auspicious circumstance, he had finally reached the moment when he stood on the threshold of his goal. A glow must have radiated from his face as he stepped out of the river. He accepted a bowl of gruel offered him by a village girl, sat on a cushion of grass piled up for him by a village boy, and entered into meditation. In other words, his mind and body alike were in peak condition for achieving the Great Awakening. Indeed, if credit is to be given where due, the six years of ascetic practice must be recognized as having made an indispensable contribution to his state of preparedness.

On December 8, when the prince was thirty-five years old and the morning star shone with exceptional brilliance, "the eyes of man" were opened at last. At that moment, it is said, he burst out:

Oh, how wondrous! how wondrous!
All things in heaven and on earth
bear within themselves from the outset
the numinous aspect of enlightenment!

This was "the discovery of paradise." In this moment mankind discovered an eternal paradise. When, in enlightenment, man's eyes are opened, he is able to enter the luminous, majestic world of eternal reality, a world without sin, sickness, or death.

But what does it mean to see with "eyes of enlightenment"? What is it that enables us to recognize the world of eternal reality? This is due to the truth called "the three seals of the dharma." These three seals, the "three truths that Buddha never for a moment forgot," are as follows: "all phenomena are transient, all beings are devoid of substance, nirvana is bliss." Of the three, the first and third had already been discovered before Buddha's time. This is clear from the Upanishads and other scriptures. The truth of "non-substance" or "non-self" is therefore the only dharma seal discovered by Buddha. In other words the result of his six years of excruciating austerities was the discovery of the single truth of "non-self." When we who are followers of Buddha understand that this the only truth grasped by Buddha after concentrating all his wisdom and energy, then we too must devote all our strength to the perfect understanding of this truth. It is no exaggeration to say that the forty-five years of Buddha's missionary life were dedicated to the propagation of this one truth. His last words were: "He who sees this truth sees me."

Buddha's remains were left to his disciples as a handful of ashes. By the same token, the truth of non-self was "the ashes of his mind." In later years this truth came to be known as "truth ashes," and stupas built all over the world enshrine this recognition with the inscription "truth ashes."

This is an appropriate place for us to take a second, deeper look at the name "Shakya-muni Buddha." "Shakya," as indicated above, is the name of the Buddha's clan. It was the custom, in his day, to use the name of the region or clan when addressing a person respectfully. It is quite natural, therefore, that Siddhartha should have been called "Shakya." But this does not explain why the clan name became part of his formal title.

The word "Shakya" itself suggests a meaning of great value. From ancient times "Shakya" has been interpreted as "mighty love." "Mighty" means omnipotent and om-niscient, a freely creative power, and one who possesses it without limit is called "god." What is the aim of Buddhism? Seen from outside, Buddhism can be described as aiming at *unrestricted freedom*. This is what other religions generally express with the word "god." It must be said that "mighty" is indeed the highest idea of every man. When it comes to explaining the word "love," the greatly venerated Confucius is the sole master in the field, but what he really means is the same as Christian love or Buddhist compassion.

Man's happiness, precisely defined, can be expressed as "freedom and love." Man is happy when he feels loved or free. Consequently, unhappiness indicates lack of love or freedom. To become happy, one needs only to fan to flame the emotion of love and the sense of freedom. This makes it a clear and simple matter to give a definition for "para-dise." Paradise is a "realm of infinite freedom and love." Shakya discovered a paradise of freedom and love and lived in accordance with it. This fact, though having a beauty and charm of its own, must have become attached to the name "Shakya" and treasured within the hearts of the disciples.

The Hindu word "Muni," on the other hand, means "saintly hermit." As such, I believe it here denotes Shakya, the great practitioner of asceticism, during the period immediately preceding his enlightenment. So even if Siddhartha had not achieved bud-dhahood, the name "Shakyamuni" would in all likelihood have been recorded in the annals of history.

At this point the greatness of Buddha presents itself with unmistakable clarity. Rigorous self-introspection did not lead him to rest content with the way he was. Entering alone the forest of Buddhagaya, he eventually became a buddha. "Buddha" means "one whose eyes are open," one whose eyes have been opened to the law of non-self. A distinct contrast between the words "muni" and "buddha" emerges here. But in Shakya's case both words had to be used side by side. One word could not stand for the other. He was great as a muni, and even greater as a buddha. It is doubtless for this reason that he bore the title "Shakyamuni Buddha."

Shakya was indeed a muni and a buddha. He was outstanding in practice and unsurpassed in wisdom. If he had been outstanding in practice but lacking in wisdom, he would have been blind, and if outstanding in wisdom but short on practice, he would have been a cripple. But the sacred words are utterly appropriate: "Eyes of wisdom, feet of practice." The name "Shakyamuni Buddha" teaches this to his followers and will doubtless do so forever.

## Principle of the Oneness of Body and Mind

RELIGION THAT PENETRATES TO THE DEPTHS OF ONE'S BEING

"I have to go tomorrow for a test to get my driver's license renewed. What a drag!" My friend heaved a sigh.

"What are you worried about? You've been driving for years. It should be easy for you."

"When I test myself at home, it's a breeze. But as soon as I enter the examination room, I'm lost. I take my Bible along, keep it before me on the table, and pray before answering the questions, but I always fail two or three times before they renew my license."

This lady had been driving for about thirty years, so she had probably taken the test at least seven times already. She was also a devout person, and I know she went to church several times a week. So I replied, "That's a shame. I'll tell you what to do. After you finish praying, take ten deep breaths, moving your abdomen like this"…and I demonstrated. "Be sure to do it tomorrow." All this took place in less than five minutes.

The next night, the phone rang. "Reverend, thank you so much. For the first time in my life, I passed the test on the first try!"

Not too many Christians are as devout as this women. Yet at times of stress, her pulse would become rapid and she could not control her nervousness. After only a few minutes training in breathing, however, she learned to control herself—and passed the test!

The effectiveness of the breathing method is not limited to passing examinations. It is a marvelous method adaptable to all life's problems. In the Orient they have the saying *sono kokyū de*. Literally translated it means "do it with that kind of breath," but in practice it means "that's the way." The way we breathe can make a difference not only in how we do our work, engage in artistic pursuits, or enter into games, but also in our relationships with people, in the curing of our ailments, and in the prevention of accidents. Many consequences can be traced to how we breathe.

Religion is generally thought of as a "way of mental (or spiritual) attitudes," but this characterization cannot be applied either to Yoga or to Buddhism. Along with inner attitudes, they also teach a counterpoise: physical attitudes. This is readily seen in the experience of the woman mentioned above. Her thirty years of devout faithfulness could not accomplish what a minute of the breathing method did.

Yoga and Buddhism, though originally belonging to the general category of religion, were quick to grasp the law that "the mind or spirit of man is governed by his body." As a result they delved deeply into the study of the body. Whereas Western medicine studied the body in order to cure physical ills, the followers of Yoga and Buddhism did so in order to become divine. To achieve this goal, they decided that fifty percent of one's energy should be expended on mental attitude and fifty percent on physical. Zen, the most important feature of Yoga Buddhism, begins with physical attitude and then moves to the mental. It does not restrict itself to the mental alone. I urge you to try it and discover for yourself what a blessing it is for human beings that a religion that penetrates to the depths of one's being, a truly human religion based on the oneness of body and mind, bloomed in India twenty-five hundred years ago.

## CUTTING LOOSE FROM BLIND FAITH

Religion exists, supposedly, to save mankind. But what most religions mean by "man" seems a shallow thing. There is no such thing in this world as a man with a mind but no body or a body but no mind. Without exception, every person has both. Even a sheet of paper has both a front side and a back. "Bring me a piece of paper with only a front and no back, please." What an impossible request! Man too, his mind and body, form an inseparable coexistence. Yet most religions seem to think of the body and mind as completely separate entities.

A friend of mine, highly respected in the community, was walking along the street one night when an assailant jumped out from a side street and hit him repeatedly on the head with a hammer. He was taken to the hospital unconscious. Fortunately, his physical wounds healed, but from that time on, he was a changed man. Formerly a gently person, now he was hot-tempered. A skilled swordsman with every faculty under complete control, now he was incontinent. This incident turned him into a useless being—and forced me to make a rapid about-face in my conception of man.

Faith, personality, or morality can be destroyed instantly by a physical change. The commonly accepted idea that the mind has an existence of its own quite apart from the body is, I discovered, a dogmatism of blind faith. I also found that to protect the mind, one must always protect the body. This was what lay behind my conversion to Yoga Buddhism.

## MIND IN THE FORMATION OF THE BODY

"The mind forms the body and the body the mind. The two are not to be separated." This is the basic principle of Yoga.

"The mind forms the body" means that any change in the mind will invariably effect a change in the body as well. When you think about raising your hand, your hand rises, and when you feel you want to turn your head, it turns. These occurrences are of course quite natural, but it is noteworthy that the image produced in the mind was reproduced faithfully by the body.

There is a psychologist who acquired sudden fame by announcing his discovery that it is not sadness that makes people cry but crying that makes people sad. This way of putting it would seem to suggest that the body takes the lead and the mind follows, but this is not what is meant. What he was trying to say is that whether the initiative comes from body or mind, the interreaction is so simultaneous that it is difficult to tell which comes first. One cries because of sadness in the mind, then the mind is affected by the bodily function of crying and becomes even sadder, and the increase in sadness makes one cry still more.

This way of looking at things can be applied to other things as well. "It is not because something is funny that we laugh. Laughing makes it funny." Thus it is that when we listen to a comedian, we find that the laughter becomes stronger and more spontaneous toward the end of the show than at the beginning.

According to Dr. Satoshi Hara, his mother once suffered chronic diarrhea. She went to many doctors but found no relief, so finally Dr. Hara decided to study the illness and cure her. He was already a middle-aged, well-established physicist and entrepreneur, but he withdrew from the business world and entered medical school. One subject on which he did research involved an experiment on the effect of emotions on the blood. He found that when a man is made angry, his blood acidifies and its viscosity instantly increases, but when he is led to feel gratitude, his blood turns alkaline and its viscosity decreases. His experiments proved that blood quality changes rapidly in correlation with a man's emotional states.

The wife of a close friend suffered a stroke and was paralyzed for a long time. She had been a very active person, so one morning when she did not get out of bed, her husband tried to waken her, but there was no response. She had suffered a stroke during the night. Just the evening before, the couple had had a heated argument over the education of their child. Anger increases the viscosity of the blood, but the brain demands its customary supply. This means that thick, sticky blood must be forcibly circulated. Just as a balloon filled to excess will burst, so a small artery in the brain can break and cause one to live out his years as an invalid. According to my doctor friend, over half the strokes people suffer occur after a heated emotional difficulty.

Impurity of the blood is related not only to strokes but to illnesses of all kinds, including the common cold. Cancer can be prevented if the blood is clear. When this pathological principle is truly understood, people will recognize the importance of "composure of the blood" and, directly connected to it, "composure of the mind."

When one's mind or spirit is fashioned anew by religion, sickness is healed. This is perfectly natural, even though some regard such a view as superstitious. Such arrogance and lack of introspection! Fortunately, however, a recent development that goes by the name of psychosomatic medicine concentrates on changing inner attitudes in order to cure illnesses.

Correcting inner attitudes will heal some sicknesses but not necessarily all. In a word, experience shows that half of people's illnesses can be cured through correcting mental attitudes, but the other half require the correction of physical factors.

There is one point that all of us must understand. If a soldier falls injured on the battlefield, a buddy picking him up will say, "Keep your courage up! It's not serious." Even if the buddy knows the wound is serious, perhaps even fatal, it is only human that he should try to encourage the wounded man. Suppose someone were to say, "You're badly wounded. It seems critical." Can you imagine the effect? A religious person will follow the first course. His purpose is to encourage and give life. So even to a critically ill person he will give hope. "God will heal you." No one should criticize a person trying to give help in this way by calling him a liar or unscientific.

I once had a friend who was a swashbuckling giant of a man. He often took me out to Chinese restaurants. One bowl of rice was more than enough for me, but he would gulp down three bowls and then say, "So far, all the food has disappeared into thin air; from now on, I'm going to feed my stomach." Then he would start on his fourth bowl. It was fascinating watching him put away such vast amounts of food with apparent relish. His voice was loud and deep. He was a he-man type who just laughed it off when a thief pointed a pistol at him.

One day my friend walked to the office of a nearby doctor because of nagging abdominal pains. Since they were on friendly terms and since the doctor knew him to be a heroic, brave type, he blurted out, "This could well be cancer." Instantly the man dropped into a chair and became unable to move. He feebly asked the doctor to call a taxi even though his home was only a block away. Six months later he died of cancer of the liver. I officiated at the funeral. The doctor was also a good friend of mine, and it was he who sadly related to me what had taken place in his office.

In cases of malignant cancer should a doctor be honest with the patient? This problem is still debated today. In considering such problems it is essential for the people involved to take a positive attitude. Sometimes it is better not to tell the patient, perhaps because of something about the patient himself or because of his circumstances. At other times it may be better to tell him. A doctor knows better than others that medical science is not omnipotent. Some doctors, by telling the patient, arouse a great determination within him. One patient may serenely make preparations for his approaching death. Another may seek some way, like Yoga, to cure himself. This latter way requires that the patient himself face up to the situation and apply himself and thus calls for conditions that will spur him to diligent effort.

## BODY IN THE FORMATION OF THE MIND

"Reverend, our older children pay no attention to our anxieties and stay out till late at night. The younger ones are always fighting. I've read many books on child psychology and education, but I've found no solution. What can I do?"

I am not a dog, but I sniffed and tried to sense her body odor.

"At your home, do you eat eggs, meat, white bread, and sweets every day?"

"Yes, we do. How can you tell?"

"Does your husband complain of stiff shoulders and look moody?"

The woman looked surprised and nodded assent. I fast quite often. This has made my nose extraordinarily sensitive. People with stomach trouble, bad liver, or feminine problems all possess a unique odor. People who overindulge in eggs and meat, though they may not be sick now, have an unpleasant odor.

"Talk it over with your husband, and from tonight, change your diet. Because their blood is impure, your children may be unhappy for a while, but if you continue this vegetarian diet, their blood will become clear, and eggs and meat will become distasteful to them. Then they will have become obedient and gentle children."

I proceeded to show her the four basics of the diet. "First, all seeds, such as brown rice. Second, raw vegetables. Third, edible sea plants or laver. Fourth, small fish that can be eaten whole. Eat all these impartially. The children will not only benefit for the rest of their lives, but your husband's problems will also fade away."

Three weeks later, the results were already evident. I received a happy and grateful phone call.

"Food is life." So said a master yogi. That a man's life is determined by his food is a truth that will continue unaltered as long as man subsists on food. A child with ignorant parents is pitiful. A newborn babe has the glow of an angel. But ignorant, unenlightened parents keep feeding him improper foods, and finally he turns into a delinquent. The quality of the blood is determined by food. Blood quality is, in its own way, one's "mind." Calcium deficiency makes fidgety children. Lack of vitamin B will make a child lazy. There are nearly twenty chief vitamins and more than half as many minerals. A man's character is greatly affected by the amounts of each that he ingests.

Education, education—let us free ourselves from the illusion that we can educate our children through the mind alone. "The body forms the mind." This peerless wisdom was discovered by yogi masters centuries ago.

## BODY, MIND, AND THE MULTIPLICATION PRINCIPLE

Body and mind are like the left and right legs. By working together, they make walking possible. Walking on one foot is not altogether impossible. You can hop. A rabbit hops with both feet and escapes. I once heard of a one-legged man who figured that a person should be able to adapt to one-leggedness and hopped about without the help of an artificial leg or crutches. But they say he died young.

However devout and pious you may be, you cannot expect to live a long and healthy life if you eat such foods as white bread and meat everyday, just because you like them. In the same way, however enthusiastically you may practice health methods, you cannot expect to live a long and healthy life if you harbor an evil mind or hatred.

There are people, however, who reason that if one is *truly* devout, he will naturally start avoiding bad foods. If one is *thorough* in his practice of health methods, all bad thoughts will vanish. Such people assert that the trouble arises from not being thorough.

They doubtless think that even though the paths to the summit are many, the moon visible at the peak is one.

It is possible, of course, to climb to the top of Mt. Fuji on one leg. Depending on faith without health methods or on health methods without faith is exactly like trying to climb a mountain with one leg. From birth we have been given the two legs of "body" and "mind." We have also been given the two shoes of religion and medicine. Walking while wearing shoes on each foot must be considered the best method.

It should be clearly understood that body and mind are based on the principle of yin and yang. The relation between them is like that between man and woman. A husband and wife are generally thought of in accordance with the idea that one plus one equals two. Anyone knows, however, that this kind of one plus one can soon equal three or four. When a couple truly becomes one, new life is created. This is not to say that if body is one and mind one, their power is doubled when one is added to each. On the contrary, when these two are combined, a strength beyond our comprehension comes into being.

The same can be said of the leg. As compared to running on one leg, running on two legs is not just double speed. It can be ten times faster or even more.

The reason body and mind must never be separated is tied up with this insight. It can be called the "multiplication principle." Yin and yang underlie the multiplication principle. When the two are combined, power is created not by addition but by multiplication. This being understood, it is inconceivable that body and mind should be considered as separate categories.

After World War II, the Reverend Doshin So revived in Japan the art of Shorinji *kenpō* as taught by the holy sage Dharma. In thirty years, he trained some 600,000 people in this art. In the immediate postwar period when morale among Japanese people was at its lowest, how was it that he penetrated quickly into every corner of the country? Outwardly, *kenpō* is nothing but putting the body through its paces. But Reverend So, quite rightly, gave strong emphasis to the mind. This must naturally have brought the multiplication principle into play and evoked new confidence in the hearts of those who entered upon this way. Judo, fencing, aikido, karate—all emphasize the mind. But none can compare to *kenpō*.

## Points Neglected in Religion and Medicine

### BECOMING AWARE OF CULTURE AS SHAPER OF "MAN"

To say that a man possesses both mind and body is entirely different from saying he possesses a hat and shoes. Putting on a big hat will not make his shoes larger, and changing from black shoes to brown will not change the color of the hat. Between hats and shoes there is no direct connection, so you go to a milliner to buy a hat and to a shoe store to buy shoes. But the relation between mind and body is altogether different. Mind and body can no more be separated than your face and its reflection in the mirror. If you smile, the face in the mirror will smile too—even when you don't want it to. If you smiled but the mirrored face wore a frown, something would be radically wrong. In the same way when the mind smiles, the body smiles as well. Who can deny this? If you feel well physically, you will also feel well mentally. Who will say this is wrong? Try an experiment. When you feel happy, can you put an angry look on your face? When you are angry inside, can you smile? Even an actor, though this is not the best of examples, cannot laugh or cry unless he first puts himself in the mood.

This shows that the relation between body and mind is a relation of oneness. But how, then, did they come to be separated? Why did it become the natural thing to go to a physician for physical problems and to a religious leader for help in matters of the spirit? Through all mankind's cultural history, no mistake can have been greater than this. One can think of all kinds of mistakes—mutual misunderstandings between capitalism and communism, misuse of the atomic bomb, mistakes by labor unions, mistakes in the insurance system, mistakes in policies for the prevention of traffic accidents. Because of the confusion in man's heart, many big mistakes are going about undetected in broad daylight. But the mistake that separates body and mind is greater than them all.

The reason for this is that all human culture has *man* as its foundation. If man becomes magnificent, his culture will inevitably become magnificent. If man becomes a failure, his culture and everything else will also go downhill.

Whenever a socialist opens his mouth, he says, "A man becomes bad because society is bad." If so, then society must be reformed. But society cannot reform itself. Someone has to do it. And who is this "someone"? It can only be man himself. An elephant has immense strength, but it would be useless to go to the zoo and ask the elephant to under- take the task. The same is true not only as regards problems of social structure but also as regards all problems having to do with human culture. Only *man* can improve his culture. When man becomes great, culture will become great.

Religion and medical science are directly involved in this "making of man." Religion shapes him inwardly and medical science builds up his body.

An abrupt statement like this may raise some doubts. Is most religion today ready for this task? Is today's medical science really prepared to build up man's body? This is the nub of the problem. Today, most people think of a priest as one who officiates at funerals and of a physician as one who hands out drugs—a far cry from what was originally intended. The religion I advocate is one that maintains its original features, one dedicated to the shaping of the inner man or the heart; and the medical science I mean is one that holds fast to its original form, one dedicated to the building up of man's body.

Original religion and medicine—why did they stray so far from their paths? To reflect on this matter, and correct it, is the focal point of this book.

## SAD FATE OF RELIGIOUS LEADERS AND PHYSICIANS

Children are honest. This is true all over the world. But as they become adults, they start to tell lies. This too is true all over the world. Why is this?

"Who chopped down the cherry tree?" "I did." The honest answer came from George Washington, but nowhere is it noted whether he was scolded or spanked. Washington was able to respond honestly because he was inherently honest, but that is not the only reason. He must also have come from a good family of deep understanding. No matter how honest a child may be, if he is scolded every time he speaks honestly, that will put an end to his honesty. When people start thinking they will come out on the short end if they are honest, they will soon start thinking of ways to fool others. I believe the same psychological process is involved in the gradual degeneration of religion and medicine.

Religion and medicine were both very pure in their developmental state. Shakyamuni, Jesus, and many other founders of religious movements were revered and called saints. Pien-ch'üeh, Hippocrates, and many other great doctors were venerated as saintly healers. Words like "saint" and "saintly" are fitting only when used for outstanding physicians and religious people; they are misused when applied to people in other fields. Thus it was that the purity in the lives of these religious men and doctors led people to revere them and apply to them the word "saint."

In later years, however, the names "doctor" and "priest" came to be almost dirty words. Like "bonze" or "quack," they are hardly terms of praise. I can think of two reasons this happened. First, past masters had attained such a high stage that while it was possible to copy them outwardly, it was impossible to match them in substance. It must have produced an impression like that of a monkey wearing a top hat. A drunken priest in silks and brocades, or a doctor with the sniffles making his hospital rounds with assistants in tow, is not a pretty sight. Some cynics say this is only to be expected since priests and doctors are human too. But the public has a sharp eye for appraisals and will not be blinded.

Second, though doctors and religious leaders apply themselves diligently, as the years pass their work shows fewer and fewer results. This is an inevitable consequence of the conditions under which they work. In the past man's life was much closer to nature. There were no enriched grains or refined sugars. Fish were not made poisonous with mercury and vegetables were not sprayed with pesticides. Bread and soy sauce easily became moldy because they contained no preservatives. Summers were hot and winters cold because there were no air conditioners or heaters. Men had to walk wherever they went. It was truly a healthful life, one we can be envious of today. Consequently, people did not suffer from high blood pressure or cancer. According to Dr. D—, there were no diabetics in Japan in the years immediately following World War II, so even though there were lectures on diabetes in the medical schools, there were no experiments. It was a time when there was little food and no refined rice or sugar. People existed mainly on potatoes—when they could get them. They could not have become diabetic even if they had wanted to. This shows what a decisive role food plays in determining man's health. In earlier days man enjoyed the same health as the beasts in the wilderness. When the body is healthy, the mind is naturally healthy too. So even though religious leaders did not try too hard, most people were able without difficulty to retain a deep faith. This was doubtless a great source of satisfaction and encouragement to religious leaders as human beings.

The same can be said of the physician. In the past man had a more gentle and willing spirit. In Japan when people got up in the morning they paid their respects to the sun;

even a drink of water was taken with gratitude. Not only those pilgrims making the rounds of the eighty-eight sacred sites of Shikoku but also all people on their way to a place of worship anywhere in Japan were welcomed and given shelter in private homes. When the spirit is healthy, the body is naturally healthy too. Thus with comparatively simple treatments from the doctor, afflictions were easily cured, giving happiness and confidence to doctors as human beings.

But today, as a result of our so-called cultured life, the body has become unnatural. Consequently, what a minister does in a casual way to help others is like pounding nails into sawdust. Sometimes he is even greeted with the words "I don't want to be preached at." In the same way, as a result of their so-called graduation from schools, people's minds have become unnatural. They do not go to school to acquire knowledge but to get a sheet of paper called a diploma. Unless the test questions are answered in accordance with the teacher's opinion, they may fail, so they sit through the lectures even when they are boring. But if the time of youth, the most important period for building character, is spent in such a spiritless manner, what kind of adults will they turn out to be? Doctors are to be sympathized with for having to treat people with such unnatural minds. Even correct treatment will not necessarily bring about good results.

Thus it is that religious leaders and physicians are impeded by their era, cannot fulfill their expectations, and fall into disappointment. This naturally leads them to neglect their true path. As one critic put it deploringly, "When doctors gather, they discuss moneymaking; when priests gather, they talk about women." What a tragic era!

## Breaking Out of the Impasse

In times past, religious leaders' belief in the worthwhileness of their work rested on the fact that people possessed healthy bodies. Doctors found fulfilment in their profession because people had healthy minds. This means that the greatest concern of religious leaders today should be the rebuilding of healthy bodies, and the main interest of physicians should be the recovery of healthy minds. The inference that *seems* to be suggested is that ideally ministers and physicians should work side by side, as in a three-legged race. But as things presently stand, they could not do so even if they so desired.

Take, for example, the man who goes to a doctor's office. Even if the doctor were to tell him to go see a minister and be treated inwardly, the desired result simply would not be forthcoming. Likewise, if a minister told a believer who had come to him for help to go to a doctor, the outcome would be the same.

What, then, is the solution? One man must perform the work of both doctor and minister. Not a three-legged race but one person with two good legs that always work together any time and any place.

"Doctor and minister in one person"—this is hardly a new idea. In an earlier day, religious leaders made full use of the medical knowledge available in their time and healed the sick. Ministers were always physicians, and physicians were always religious leaders. There were of course differences between individuals. In some, it was the religious side that came out more strongly; in others, the greater emphasis appeared in physical healing.

But the initial desire, to be a doctor and minister at one and the same time, was always at work. Look up the words and deeds of the great physicians of the past. They were more religious than most religious leaders today. "This medicine was bestowed upon us by the gods. Drink it with reverence." Words like these are more than adequate to portray to us the attitude of doctors in bygone days. In fact I can remember seeing my grandmother always reverently bow her head before drinking medicine. But today's doctors are more likely to say, "What works is the medicine itself. What's the point of bowing to it?"

In old Japan there was a tradition that loquat trees should be planted only in temple yards, not in the yards of private homes. Almost every temple thus had at least one loquat tree in the garden. The reason was that loquat leaves, according to Chinese medicine, were good for almost any malady. Things were set up so that if a person became sick, he would go and worship at the temple. In later years, however, it came to be considered "bad luck to plant loquat trees." This saying tells us much about why Buddhism has fallen, unnecessarily, into decline. The temple of older times cultivated many herbs within its compounds, and in point of fact, priests had to be physicians too.

For religion to fulfill its original purpose, and for medical science to realize its original objective, both must return to the ancient norm of "the oneness of medicine and religion." Anyone who decries this as a return to a primitive state or as utterly impossible of realization can only be said to have misunderstood what religion and medicine are really about.

## "Doctor and Minister in One Person"

"Religion and medicine, each taken in its own right, are already difficult; for one person to practice them concurrently is impossible"—this is the voice of common sense. Admittedly, religion and medicine must be the most difficult and time-consuming of professions to master. One can readily imagine that if a person were to attempt both, he would be old and gray before he could hang out his shingle.

"It is impossible for a wingless human to fly." This was common sense a hundred years ago. Even twenty years ago it was generally accepted that for a man to go to the moon was impossible. Thanks to the few who were aware of the possibilities and carried out extensive research, the space age came into being. The ideal of a doctor and minister in one person may be contrary to common sense now, but I believe that day will come—and much sooner than we imagine.

What I have in mind, of course, is not religion or medicine as we see it generally practiced today. From this starting point, the goal would not be realized even if we waited a hundred years. The religion and medicine I am talking about is altogether different.

To become a professional in religion, one must go to a seminary. In Buddhism many years are spent learning the Pali and Sanskrit languages, tongues not even in use today. Likewise in Christianity the same can be said of the study of Hebrew and Latin. What value is there in this for a religion devoted to saving living people? A religious person does not need to be a scholar. If a man could be saved by hearing Sanskrit or Latin, I would be singing quite a different song, but nothing quite so miraculous has been heard of to date.

Because they are compelled to study unnecessary and uninteresting subjects for many years, hopeful youths often turn into humdrum clergymen. Research, of course, is essential. But continued research can be left to professionals. What is most necessary to young people aspiring to religious leadership is to come in direct contact with the teachings and personalities of great religious people now actually engaged in saving the masses. There are twenty or thirty such people worth listening to in any country. Have them conduct classes. The rest will follow very simply. Capable religious leaders will start appearing within a short time and will continue to appear thereafter. During the period of their training, sectarianism must be forgotten. Emphasis must be placed on "seeking the truth."

But what about the medical shools? Their graduates are very learned in non-essentials and have failed to study what is most important. Medical students pay high tuitions and go to school for seven long years, but one wonders if the time and money was well spent. Microscopes, test tubes, dissecting of dead humans, experiments on mice and guinea pigs —all this is necessary. Diagnosing ailments is also necessary. Medicine and surgery are also necessary at times, so they too must be studied.

But placing a microscope beside a patient has never been known to cure high blood pressure. Diagnosing an ailment as cancer has never caused cancer to disappear. Today's physicians must consider carefully this simple point. A priest for forty years, I have officiated at many funerals. It is a sorry task to have to say a requiem for a person who has died in the prime of life. If he loses his life in an accident, it is another matter, but most have been under the care of physicians. I have also visited many patients in the hospitals. I see them suffering from continuous injections and transfusions, a practice that seems to have become more extreme in recent years. "Please ask them to let me go home," many patients have pleaded with me. But the doctors always say, "Not yet." Even the patient's family members have the same thought. As a result, many patients pass away in the hospital. Some have a premonition of approaching death and beg to die in their own homes, but this final wish is cruelly ignored.

This is no time for the medical profession to use the law as a shield. Nor is it a time to treat Western medicine as the only form of medical science. Former President Nixon visited the People's Republic of China not long ago. His grasp of current trends was most acute, but he returned with an unexpected bonus: acupuncture, a branch of Eastern medicine. "Incurable disease cured without pain by acupuncture." "Surgery performed without anesthesia." "Miracle of the Orient," etc. Newspapers played up this new discovery with headlines and articles. Compared to a few years ago when people were convicted for practicing acupuncture, it seems like a different age. Acupuncture has been practiced for thousands of years as Oriental medicine and praised and treasured by the people. Oriental medicine never tried to hide it or keep it a secret. Why then was it ignored for so long? This fact might tell a little about the character of present-day Western medicine.

In my opinion, acupuncture is only a small part of Oriental medicine. There are others that are more valuable. Its breathing method, its diet, its herbal prescriptions, its skin strengthening method, its body alignment method—all these are medically more valuable than acupuncture. From about ten years ago, Yoga exercises, part of the body alignment method, have finally come to be understood by Western medicine, but the essence of Oriental medicine is not understood to this day.

The world has become smaller. Traffic between East and West has become more frequent, but still Western physicians do not try to study this great Oriental medicine. Why? To put it more precisely, why do the physicians avoid using it? I will give one example and you can answer the question yourself.

This example is taken from a University of Tokyo announcement titled, "A clinical study on the effect of deep breathing on high blood pressure." When patients practiced deep breathing for five minutes, six times daily, 85 percent were healed by this exercise alone. The results of the breathing method are easy to determine. Examine your blood pressure, count twice, once before deep breathing and once after taking three deep breaths. It's very simple, but you'll find a difference of about ten degrees. Let me add, no matter how many deep breaths you take, nature will not send you a bill, nor is it illegal, I believe.

In this manner, the breathing, diet, skin, and body alignment of Oriental medicine are not accompanied by danger or expense as in injections and surgery, but the results are outstanding. The necessity for, and the great contributions made by Western medicine in cases of injuries sustained in accidents, medication for emergency cases, and for control of special contagious diseases must not be overlooked or underestimated. But the great majority of patients do not come under this category. They are more apt to suffer chronic ailments. I understand that an ailment not cured in three months is considered chronic. We must honestly acknowledge the fact that most sick people are in this class. This is the point where Oriental medicine comes into play. For several thousand years, Oriental medicine has been dealing with chronic disorders. As they say, "The proof of the pudding is in the eating." This can be demonstrated anytime, any place.

Now this calls for serious consideration on the part of medical colleges. Academics should be left to the scholars. If actually healing the physical sufferings of living men is the original and principal aim of physicians, then doctors themselves should experience and experiment with Oriental medicine and see the results. To study and master it will not require a long period. If you train and study under the guidance of first class Oriental medicine masters, two years are sufficient.

Therefore, I am convinced that in about four years, that is, two years study of the essence of religion and two years of medicine, a full fledged, no-risk "doctor and minister in one person" can be trained. With the unique power of religion and medicine instilled into him simultaneously, with this concentrated attack, he should be ready for any problem of mental or physical suffering. At this time, the importance of the "multiplication principle" must be reaffirmed. Take, for instance, "Hopkins Law." According to this law, a water current of $x$ force can wash away a rock weighing one pound; if the force of the current is doubled, it can wash away a 64-pound rock; if the force is tripled, a rock weighing 729 pounds will be washed away. Why floods cause so much devastation is now comprehensible. Now man has two aspects, the mind and the body. What will happen when both aspects simultaneously become healthy through the work of men who are at once doctors and ministers? Figuring simply, the health current is doubled, but the power to wash away the rock of affliction will be many times stronger. It is only natural that the

Yoga masters of the past claimed that any sickness could be made to disappear.

I think that because the religionist strayed from his original path, the physicians stopped expecting anything from him, and the same can be said of the physician. Actually, today's physician holds no love for the religionist and vice versa. Doctors warn, "Don't be fooled by the claim that faith heals," and religionists say, "Don't inject your god-given body with medication." It cannot be denied that there is a faint smell of professional hostility in this. Mutual reflection seems to be needed here, and instead of mutual cooperation, I believe the time has now come for the opening of a new way of saving man, namely, through training physico-religious therapists.

Also, there is another factor to be considered, a factor supporting the view that when religion and medicine are studied simultaneously, a short training period of four years, two of religion and two of medicine, is sufficient. This factor is that when you study religion, you naturally begin to understand one phase of medicine and when you study medicine you naturally begin to understand one phase of religion. Correct religion will always lead to medicine, and correct medicine will always lead to religion. This is because man's body and mind has a relationship that can never be separated.

Why not put it to the test? If an occupation named "physico-religious therapy" should emerge, not only illness but also crime, poverty, accidents, divorces, strikes, and war would become extremely rare, and buildings now used as hospitals, prisons, and arsenals, becoming unnecessary, would be converted into schools or turned to recreational uses.


# The Way of Body and Mind:
# Norm for Revolutionizing Man

### BUDDHISM AS THE WAY OF BODY AND MIND

Take a look at the problem of war. All people dislike war. But if they hate it so much, why don't they stop fighting instead of getting into one war after another?

I have attended many meetings for the establishment of a worldwide commonwealth of nations. On the way home, I always feel sad. Representatives attending the meetings all harbor a fervent desire for world peace. But how few of them actually possess inner peace. I participated in these meetings because I thought it better to have meetings than to do nothing. There are many who argue for peace. But a possessor of peace is as rare as stars in the sky at dawn.

The builder of peace is, in short, man himself. Unless man is at peace within himself, there is no basis on which to begin to build world peace. This is the reason for my advocacy of "physico-religious therapy." The existence of mind and body in man is not like two horses hitched side by side pulling a buggy, but like two streams flowing into one indissoluble current empowered by the multiplication principle.

The words of people who preach peace without possessing inner peace are bound to contain flaws, and such people, lacking a peaceful mind, also lack a "peaceful body." A peaceful mind cannot dwell in a body deficient in vitamins C or E, or lacking in calcium or silicon. The reverse is also true. Even though one may have a peaceful body, if he lacks a peaceful mind, he can never become a peaceful man. Even though one discusses peace with his lips, it must be emphasized that he does not necessarily have a peaceful mind. Peace is not established by a peaceful mind or a peaceful body, but, indeed, is established by a peaceful man. Therein lies the reason I cannot help but emphasize "physico-religious therapy."

Disintegration of families, labor disputes, traffic accidents, vicious crimes, incurable diseases—these are all serious problems which must be solved for the sake of man's happiness, but like the peace problem, mankind's present state is similar to that of a spectator at a fire disaster where there is insufficient water. This is why we need a new way, the "physico-religious" way. I have ventured to name it the "Way of body and mind." This phrase means: "Body and mind are essentially one and should under no circumstances be separated. If one should ever forget this and consider them separately, then he has already taken another "Way."

In the course of human history, the credit for the discovery of this way of body and mind must first be given to the yogi of India, but it was Buddhism that brought it to perfection. This history is best related by the proper noun, "Shakyamuni Buddha," as explained earlier. In the beginning Shakya was a "Sacred muni of the Yoga Way." Then he became a "Saint of the Buddhist Truth, or the Buddha."

People who read widely in the Buddhist sutras frequently come across the compound word "body-mind." That this expression is unique to Buddhism is discovered when you examine other classics of philosophy and religion. Even in the ancient "*Yoga Sutra*," you cannot find the phrase "body-mind." Therefore, it must be recognized that only Buddhism possesses the phrase "body-mind" and establishes the peerless truth of the oneness of body and mind. Of course, the relationship between mind and body has been discovered in other classics. Some claimed the body came first and the mind second, some made the reverse claim, while still others said body and mind were one. These arguments have been going on all over the world for a long time, but they all end up as nothing but a philosophical idea that never developed into a vital practice. But Buddhism, based on the principle of the oneness of body and mind, led to the practice of the oneness of body and mind. This is why the phrase "body-mind" has become an everyday word.

Religion is generally considered to deal with the heart or mind, but this is definitely not applicable to Buddhism. From its beginning to this day, it has clearly been concerned with "body-mind." For particulars, you will have to turn to my other publications, but here it may be said that the Original Buddhist teaching of the Five Aggregates (form, perception, conception, volition, and consciousness) points to the multiplication principle of the body-mind; and in the Eightfold Noble Path, the last three noble paths (correct endeavor, correct mindfulness, and correct meditation) are concerned with self practice and teach respectively correct physical practice, correct mental practice, and simultaneous correct practice of body and mind.

In this manner Buddhism is, in a logical sense, not a religion. Religion is concerned with saving the mind of man, but Buddhism saves the "man." Shakyamuni's Buddhism is concerned with saving the whole man.

"But isn't Buddhism one kind of religion after all since it too rescues men's spirits?" So some people may think. But I want to say clearly that Buddhism is not a religion. Take an honest look at the world's religions. They not only ignore the body, some actually look on it with disdain. The body is an eyesore, interfering with the mind. From the viewpoint of such religions, Buddhism can never be considered a religion. The "body-mind way" of Buddhism cannot be accused of bringing the mind and body together out of convenience. The mind is the body, and the body is the mind. They are "one" existence, inseparable. Buddhism simply accepted this naturalness without resistance.

## BASIC MISTAKE OF MODERN MEDICINE

Man is, originally, "body and mind, one person," so the cause of his illness is 50 percent physical and 50 percent mental. Of course, depending on the kind of sickness, at some times the bodily cause may be dominant and at others the mental, but when averaged, it comes out about even. It is similar to quarrels between a husband and wife. At certain times, the man can be the more guilty party, and at others the woman, but when averaged, the faults are about equal. Whenever mediating a couples's quarrel, I always give advice to both. This is only common sense, but today's medicine lacks this important common sense. How can physicians consider themselves a community for the cure of sicknesses when they ignore the mind, the mind which causes 50 percent of all illness? "Medicine is science," the physicians say boastfully. Science seeks cause and effect, and must be honest in its observations. For example, every doctor at some time must have heard the assertion that religion can heal sickness. But without seeking or observing they declare, "The belief that religion can heal sickness is an outrageous superstition." Some say, "Yes, religion is necessary, but you must not become a 'mind-onlyist.'" This sounds very reasonable, but how many doctors are there who will go on to say, "You must not be a 'body-onlyist.' You must have faith."

There is cause and there is effect. Because of a certain error, sickness results. So to erase that illness, the cause that led to the illness must be eradicated. In order to do that, the cause must be investigated thoroughly. Buddha is the One who taught us this law of cause and effect, and medical science too must be based on this law. But it seems that modern medical science is willfully avoiding this "pursuit of the cause." This is true not only in cases where the cause is mental but also in cases where it is physical.

For example, a man may be afflicted with tuberculosis. Western medicine will immediately lay the blame on tubercular germs and concentrate on killing the bacteria. But tubercular germs exist everywhere, just like cold germs, and everyone inhales them. Still, a majority is not afflicted, so the medical pursuit of the cause must be said to be very nearsighted. Since the majority is not afflicted, doctors should be instantly alerted that the true cause must lie someplace else.

Buddhism teaches that any result is the outcome of countless causes. One cause is not sufficient reason for a consequence. And among the countless reasons, we must differentiate between major and minor causes and emphasize the major. This is called *in-en*. *In* means the central cause. *En* denotes the countless conditions supporting this. So a

Buddhist, when seeking a solution, will always seek out the main cause of the problem, and dispose of it. It is said, "To control a river, one must first control the mountain." To say that the cause of a flood is low embankment is an amateur's opinion. A professional would say the main cause was that trees growing on the mountain were too sparse to regulate the flow. That tuberculosis is caused by tubercular bacteria is an amateur's viewpoint. A professional must necessarily know that it was caused by a ruptured capillary blood vessel.

"There is a body. If it has no flaw, poison cannot harm it. Poison is harmless before perfection. Where there is no defect, there is no basis for producing it."

The above is a passage from the *Dhammapada* (section 124). If a man is bitten by a poisonous snake, the poison, it is said, must be sucked out by mouth immediately. If there are no wounds inside the mouth, sucking the poison will not cause any harm. In pulmonary tuberculosis, it is not the germ that should be dreaded but the wound inside the lung. The hemorrhage of the capillary tube within the lung is the cause. Therefore, the aim of the treatment must be to first repair the rupture of the capillary tube. Actually, without even attempting to kill the germs, but simply by practicing Yoga, a cure can be brought about.

"I was told that I have breast cancer. What causes this?"

"It is due to a predisposition of your body."

"What can I do?"

"You must undergo an operation immediately."

I heard this conversation on a medical question-and-answer radio program. The blame for cancer is laid entirely on bodily predisposition. The question of the cause for such a predisposition is ignored and not investigated. That this is *scientific* medicine is one of the wonders of the world.

Yoga is not a "Way" to cure sickness. If *satori* or "enlightenment" is too difficult to understand, let me say it is a "Way for humans to attain the highest happiness." With this aim in mind, masters and sages have for thousands of years undergone repeated ascetic practices and self-polishing, and left us this Yoga way. And when Yoga is put into practice, illness is naturally cured.

"Do not hold mistaken notions as to how sickness can be cured. By practicing the way for men pointed out to us by our parental god, Nature, we become gods. This is the only aim." This is the Yoga understanding.

Yoga experience is not the short experiment of two or three hundred years to which Western medicine lays claim. I am not saying that old things are better, but at least where man's physiology is concerned, there is no change from past to present. Therefore, we must not treat lightly a medicinal way with thousands of years of historical background and experimentation by great masters far more serious and wise than our modern medical scientists. (Attention is invited to the author's *The Real Cause of Sickness*, to be published soon.)

## BASIC MISTAKE OF MODERN RELIGION

It seems to be the general opinion that today's people are lacking in religious faith. If it were just a lack, it would be preferable to the increase of those who insist, "There is no god." Religious leaders naturally claim that religion is a necessity. If asked, "Then why don't you go ahead and proclaim it?" they answer sadly, "Today's man will not listen." Like present-day physicians, they do not seem to want to seek out the cause of modern man's indifference to religion.

"With the rapid advancement of science, man has become captivated by science, like a child absorbed in a toy, and has no time to become interested in God," some intellectual said. But a scientist will say, "No, because of the development in science, man has acquired a mental habit of believing only things that can be proven scientifically, and since god cannot be proven, they do not believe."

A friend, who is a devout Christian, never misses a Sunday service. One Sunday, while the minister was offering a prayer, a most outrageous thought suddenly popped into his mind. "The minister looks serious and is now praying as if God were present before him. Does he really believe what he's saying?" I do not think the minister had such a bad attitude that the worshipper was led to imagine such an insolent thing. The waves of change are not visible to the eye, but they must be influencing man without his knowledge. At meetings of Buddhist priests, I always felt that only about one out of fifty had the attitude of one who truly believed in the Buddha. Whatever is in the heart always appears appears in outward form as well. Merchants may fool people with packaging and weight, but for a religious man to pretend a faith in God which he does not have is another matter.

If modern people cannot believe in anything unless it has been proven, then why don't the religionists give them actual proof?

"But God cannot be proven," they say and shrug off the question. If everyone had simply accepted the idea, "No one can talk to a person a mile away," the telephone would never have been invented. Now we can talk to anyone anywhere in the world so clearly that we almost seem to be face to face. Science certainly deserves three cheers. Due to the communication sciences, people's earnest desire for world peace has become acute, and I believe this is a service to mankind that is quite beyond the imagination of the general public. Some religious professionals claim that it is because science was mistaken that people lost faith in religion, but I disagree. It is not that science was on a high-handed, self-glorifying course, but rather that religion was dozing and did not progress side by side with science. Today, the duty awaiting the religious professionals is to "prove religion scientifically." Then even without being told to do so, today's people will believe.

I have never heard a mathematics teacher using the word "believe" to his students. If he says, "Two plus two equals four," whether they be elementary school pupils or college students, they believe alike. Even capitalists and communists believe alike. If ever it should be proposed in the U.S.S.R. that "since two plus two equals four in New York, two plus two will henceforth equal five in Moscow," the Soviet people would reject it.

"But religion is not arithmetic, so it's impossible to make it understandable to everyone." This is the kind of thinking that makes us give up easily. It has been said, "Necessity is the mother of invention." Has not a machine called an artificial brain been invented? I understand that an architectural project that would take thirty men five years to calculate, can be done by a computer in one year with only two men. If religion is as important as its professionals claim, why don't they invent a religious logic, acceptable to all, like arithmetic?

Because they have not been faithful to the honest thinking process of cause and effect, religion has committed many different mistakes. The brutal war between India and Pakistan was caused by differences between Hinduism and Islam. The tenacious struggle between Israel and the Arab nations comes also from frictions between its religions, Judaism and Islam. A friend went to Ireland to visit his aging parents. He returned a month earlier than originally planned, shaking his head. Though they are of one nation, just because of difference in religion they are killing each other. Just walking on the streets was a terrifying experience because of the machine guns on every corner. They are of the same Christian faith, but because they are of different branches of the church, blood is being shed. In mankind's long history, how many men have had to make the supreme sacrifice in the name of religion!

All religions, without exception, advocate "world peace." Yet while professing to be peacemakers, they have in fact been ringleaders of war. Like the policeman that turns robber, religion is past remedy.

"If the peace label is not a mistake, let us abolish advocating sectarianism."

"But sects were born because it was meant to be, so it cannot be helped."

"But if you keep promoting your own sect, then other sects can be expected to assert their claims, and this is sure to cause friction. Don't you realize that?"

"Then it must be mankind's fate."

What a cruel conclusion! What an ignorant and shameless feeling! Still ,the man who drew this conclusion is a respected religious leader.

A friend confessed, "I believe religion is important, but when I see the ugliness between the sects, I cannot go near a church." Past masters have also left us these words, "Religion is angelic, but sects are satanic." How many religionists are there who are seriously seeking a solution to this ugly and fearful sectarianism?

I do not mean to say that all kinds of sectarian differences are meaningless. It is a fact that at times, differences between national languages act as a hindrance to international harmony. But there is no need to criticize language because of such differences. Until the time comes when a world language is born, national languages, though inconvenient, must be treasured. Likewise, I am not saying that sects, in themselves, are bad. What is bad is the attitude of boasting about one's sect and trying to suppress the others. Eventually, man will become wiser, and a nonsectarian religion may appear that will become the faith of all mankind.

In this manner, even while still belonging to a sect, it is possible, with a little effort, to worship in a religion devoid of sectarian disposition. Why did I say "with a little effort"? Because all established churches have some pitiable hard-headed traditionalists who insist on the principle of sectarianism first, and allow humanity a poor second. The masses will not remain blind forever, however, though occasional troubles may arise and shouts of "Heretic!" and "Banishment!" may be heard.

"Let us stop referring to the paradise in the west. If we keep going west, we will just return to our point of departure and never find paradise. We are now faced with teaching the young of a scientific age. Let us strike out this old creed that is no longer necessary."

"Outrageous! Banish him!"

Thus it was that a prominent Japanese Buddhist was falsely charged and made an outcast. But time flows steadily on. Nowadays, you hardly hear a word about the "westerly direction." But I have yet to hear of an apology being made to this man by the ignorant and arrogant executive group that excommunicated him.

"Advocation of sectarianism and war are entirely different things." What an audacious thing to say! The contentious spirit of sectarianism is precisely the spirit that drives mankind to war.

Religion's mistake has continued a long time. So not being able to recognize it as a mistake seems to have become habitual in man's mind. Religionists who believe religion is for the "salvation of mind" only cause a flurry and shout charges of hereticism when I preach the "salvation of the physical body."

How numerous are the Buddhist priests ignorant of Buddhism's basic principle, "To save the mind, the body must be saved."

## DEVELOPMENT OF THE "EIGHTFOLD UNIFIED WAY"

Thorough reflection on the self is the starting point of the way of body and mind. To attain salvation, one's body and mind must be saved simultaneously. This is based on the sure and certain truth that the body and mind are as firmly connected as the head and torso, and form an inseparable existence.

For a kindergarten entrance examination, the teachers drew a circle for a human face and as usual filled it in with eyebrows, eyes, nose, and mouth, but purposely omitted one ear. "What is missing in this picture?" "The ear on this side." "Very good." "But something else is missing, teacher." "What's that?" "The body." The teacher conducting the test suddenly felt that she herself was being tested. No one has ever seen a human with only a face. But in a picture, it is common to show the face only. For an adult to whom this has become natural, just the addition of an ear would have been sufficient, but to a child who still has not become aged by habit, a human without a torso is strange. Even a ghost has a body.

It is exactly the same with body and mind. They must never be thought of as separate entities. Indian Yoga first grasped this point, and Buddhism completed it.

Let us look at the history of the Buddha. As crown prince of a nation, he was outstanding in martial arts as indicated in his biography. If it can be assumed that he was exceptionally superior in *kenpō*, then it can further be assumed that he had undergone rigorous physical training. But even six years of ascetic practices, literally centered on physical discipline, failed to satisfy truth-seeker Siddhartha. He perceived that he was lacking in inner peace. So alone, he sat under the Bodhi tree in meditation, ultimately attaining the Buddhahood which evolved into a life distinguished by forty-five years of meditation and preaching.

During that period, he firmly established many precepts, which fall into two classes: morality and the way of health. Do not eat more than one meal a day, maintain physical cleanliness by cold and warm water bathing, keep the body in tone through good posture and bodily movements, keep the living quarters clean and tidy, etc.—these are all health methods in the true sense of the word. Moreover, the meditation practice of pure Yoga is the quintessence of the health method, combining posture and breathing. Even after attaining enlightenment, Buddha was stricter in practicing the diet, cleanliness, posture and breathing precepts than any of the disciples. There was not an inkling of the jest that after one attains enlightenment, one can just drink liquor and take it easy. In his spiritual enlightenment Shakyamuni reached an unprecedented peak, but also in keeping up his physical practice, he was a saint of unparalleled achievement. Hence, through application of the body-mind multiplication principle, he ultimately became the supreme Great Saint still revered as Shakyamuni Buddha.

The Buddhism of Shakyamuni Buddha saves the whole man. Out of the desire to express this correctly and simply, I ventured to name it "the way of body and mind." Its contents are separated into eight categories, together designated the "Eightfold unified way."

The meaning of "Eightfold unified way" is "the way of body and mind uniting eight categories." This can be divided into two halves: the "four unified ways of the body," namely, breathing, diet, skin, and body alignment, and the "four unified ways of the mind," which are deliverance, mind-only, the practice of love, and ascetic training.

The expression "Buddhist Yoga" is a new one, but at the present time there seems to be no other term suitable for expressing the exquisite equilibrium of the oneness of body and mind. Because of previously accepted common ideas, using only the word "Buddhism" tends to make one think of the mind, whereas the word "Yoga" inclines us to think of physical training. Therefore, at the risk of being repetitious, I combine the two into "Buddhist Yoga." This may be understood as a type of physical training centered in the spiritual enlightenment of Shakyamuni. Actually, in India, Buddhism is regarded as a branch of Yoga. This is entirely proper, since historically and actually, the practice of meditation belongs to Yoga.

# 2.  The Way of the Body

# Necessity for the Way of the Body

## MEANING OF PHYSICAL HEALTH

*The problem of unawarenss of sickness.*   A great difference exists between the meaning of "health" as used in Buddhism and as used in Western medicine. Western doctors generally take the view that a person who has no illness and is able to work happily is healthy. "My husband had a complete physical checkup only a week ago and was pronounced totally fit, but only a few days later he had a heart attack while working and died. He was a very healthy person. Since we got married, he never had a sick day." These were the words of a grieving widow. Her husband had died at forty-seven years of age. The face of the corpse in the coffin had no wrinkles, and there was no gray in his hair.

"I have never had a doctor hold my hand. I have never caught cold, so I have never taken an aspirin. I eat well, sleep well, and have never been absent from work."

"Then you must be careful."

And I proceeded to explain why. This is the "no-sickness disease" and is found in about one out of every thousand. It is a disease if one thinks he cannot get sick. A few years ago, a friend of mine, a car mechanic, opened up the hood of his car and said, "I am always advising people to be careful and not overheat the engine, but I burned out my own. The warning light was broken. I never realized those warning lights were so important." Since then, whenever I check my engine, I always take extra precautions to check the warning lights.

Sickness is the body's warning signal. When your stomach hurts, it is "overheated," so be careful. Because the stomach was in perfect condition, it was able to go wrong. If it had already broken down, it would be incapable of registering pain, and you would then have no way of knowing you should be careful. By the time you become aware of the existence of a problem, it is too late. "No-sickness" is not necessarily good health. This is the reason people with illness often live longer.

Western medicine has a slogan, "Get a cancer checkup regularly. An early discovery saves lives." But according to a book published by an American doctor, the death rate from cancer is highest among members of the medical profession, ten times higher than that of farmers. "The ungodliness of ministers," "the tailor's wife is the worst-dressed woman in town," "the shoemaker's wife goes barefoot"—all these are well-known sayings, but this is a different matter. Whether one be a doctor or a farmer, his most important possession is life. Ungodliness and clothes have no direct connection with one's life, so one can afford to be careless. But no one can afford to be negligent where one's life is concerned. Why is it, then, that doctors have the shortest life expectancy among all professions? There must be a big mistake hidden somewhere. Sadly, not too many are aware of it.

*Becoming one who knows the day of his death.*   One master of the way of health, Mr. Katsuzo Nishi, had no peers when it came to intuitive power. If he said, "Do not ride on that ferry, its form is hazy," you were very likely to read later that the ferry had had an accident and sunk. I heard that during World War II, he saved many lives by foretelling the date, time, and place where American bombs would fall. A woman I knew once consulted Mr. Nishi. She did not disrobe for the examination, so was shocked when he said, "You have a big mole on your right lower abdomen."

"Do you think Dr. Nishi is possessed by a spirit?" she later asked.

"No, it is simply that Dr. Nishi has perfect health. Rats abandon a ship before it sails on a doomed voyage. Even before signs of a flood appear, the digger-wasp moves away. Only men cannot foretell a flood."

"How can they tell?"

"They sense it with their skin. The skin is like a television antenna. Wild creatures do not wear clothes. Their food is uncooked. They do not make the mistake of overeating. Their skin function is complete, and their receiving apparatus is not rusty. Even an antenna cannot receive properly if it is rusted. Their skins are shiny, just like new. That is how they can foretell things. We often see a cat licking his body with his tongue. He is not doing it only because he is itchy. He is sharpening up his antenna for self-protection. If you grab a cat by his four legs and drop him head down from a height of about five feet, before he touches the ground, he will twist his body around and land safely on all fours. Even at two feet, the result is the same. This is an amazing supernatural power. If it were a man, he would fall head down and come to an instant death. The ears seem to be most directly involved in this ability, but ears are also a part of the skin."

The sutra says that not only the Buddha but all those who join the ranks of Buddha's disciples will all possess six supernatural powers. These six powers are: knowing the state of the whole world without seeing it, knowing the state of the whole world without hearing about it, being able to read men's minds, being able to see the fate in store for people as if it were reflected in a mirror, being able to go wherever one desires merely by willing it, and being able to accomplish whatever one chooses. Unless one becomes endowed with these six supernatural powers, it is written that he is not qualified to call himself a disciple of Buddha.

An acquaintance once told me, "My grandmother died in a most impressive way. She was ninety-six at the time, but four days before her death, she told the family she would be bidding her last farewell in four days so she wanted all her relations and friends called. A big banquet was held with grandmother as the guest of honor. On this occasion, she danced her beloved Noh dance, saying it was her final performance. She talked as if a new year were approaching. The appointed day arrived. That morning she took a bath by herself, washed and arranged her hair, dressed in her best, asked to have her bed quilts spread out in front of the Buddhist shrine, and laid down. She said, 'You don't have to wash my body after I die,' and while quietly reciting the sutra, she passed away. During that time she had no pain or breathing difficulties, she was just the same as usual. I wish I could die like her." Then she asked, "How is it that she could predict the day of her death?"

"When Buddha's way becomes a part of you, you or anyone can do it. You know, for example, that you can decide what time you want to go to sleep, whether to retire at 10 or go to sleep at 12 p.m. In the same way you can decide the time of your eternal sleep.

This is called true health. Born as a man, how awful to have to die in an antiseptic-smelling hospital room, groaning and moaning, going through one ordeal after another—injections, transfusions, oxygen inhalator, and the rest—and after all that, not even to know when one is dying! We must not die like that."

"Health" as used in Buddhism is not just looking healthy. Even if one gets sick, one instantly rebounds and gets well with a body healthier than before. The senses of the eyes and ears are sharp. The brain functions quickly and has a deep power of understanding. One's endurance is great and his efficiency outstanding. One has strong intuitive power and is able to predict the future. The heart is as big and serene as the ocean in springtime, big with a love that cannot help but be helpful to others. These are the qualities of true health. So when you say, "Thank you, I'm fine," remember that by Buddhist standards, you may not be well at all.

## Recognizing What is Physically Unnatural

*The strain of upright posture.* Wild animals do not have a health method. They do not have doctors, pharmacists, or hospitals. They rarely become sick, but when they do, a health method appears as instinctively as a yawn and cures the illness. But man becomes sick quite often, and when he does, it takes him a long time to get well. Why is this? What are the differences between animals and people?

First, an animal walks on four legs while a man walks on two. A beast is naked, but man wears clothes. Animals do not cook their food, but man does. And there is one more important difference. You will not know this unless you have observed them, but animals move their abdomens when breathing, whereas man uses only his chest. In ancient times man's ancestors walked on all fours, and only about 60,000 years have passed since he started to walk upright on his two hind legs, the two front legs becoming "hands" to grasp things. This led to the development of his brain, which was a blessing, but at the same time created a problem. The spine easily became crooked. In building a house, if the beam supporting the roof is horizontal, the structure will be strong and sturdy. But turn the house sideways, contrary to its design, making the beam vertical, and it will collapse. From a horizontal position, man became vertical. Many thousands of years of habit are involved, so there is no fear of a sudden breakdown, but as yet, a structural strain results from walking with the spine in a vertical position. Because of this, a slight unbalance in movement or exertion of strength can cause a dislocation of some of the 33 vertebrae, which in turn can lead to sicknesses. The proof of this is that by readjusting the spine, many illnesses take an instant turn for the better when the spine is readjusted. But today we can no longer go back to walking on all fours. Therefore, it becomes necessary for man to have a special health method for correcting the spinal column.

*The unnaturalness of clothing.* When man started to wear garments, it was just another annoyance to the body. Because of clothes, the skin cannot have direct contact with the outer air and skin breathing is obstructed. The excretion of carbonic acid gas is an especially important function of the skin, and helps the lungs and kidneys in their work.

Therefore, when the skin is covered with clothes, it is just like plugging the nose or an excretory passage. Toxins accumulate in the body. Moreover, the skin functions to adjust body temperature. Man cannot survive if the body temperature is above or below a certain limit. To keep it adjusted constantly is the skin's function. When one is too hot, the skin perspires and cools, and when too cold, goose bumps appear. But because we wear clothes, these functions have become incomparably weak when compared to the beasts. (It is for the same reason that hot house plants become weak.) But we cannot walk around naked. So in order not to weaken the skin faculty, special provisions such as sun bathing and cold water rubbing become necessary.

*The unnaturalness of cooking.*   Man cannot take in as much raw green stuff or raw blood as the animals. From long, long habit, fire has been used to cook the food, and this greatly impairs the body. Minerals and vitamins die, the fibrous texture that the intestines need becomes too soft, and we become undernourished. But food is different from walking on all fours and going naked. If we have the desire and the will, we can eat the same kind of food as the animals. Those who resolutely practice this are the so-called sages and hermits. Buddha too lived like a hermit for six years. Otherwise, he would never have been able to attain the high level of enlightenment that he did.

*Unnaturalness in breathing.*   Another problem with man is that in comparison to the animals, his breathing is shallow. The reason for this is that man is burdened with schools, laws, properties, prestige, etc., things unknown in the animal kingdom. Because of this, man is always anxious or angry, and breathing is affected by the waves of these emotions. The connection between man's emotions and his breathing is similar to that between wind and waves, always in direct proportion. This is the cause of much sadness in human life. Because of the complex life he must lead, man cannot breathe ideally like the animals. Oxygen becomes scarce, carbonic acid gas accumulates, and man is driven into a state of chronic asphyxiation. That is why we must make an effort to achieve good breathing habits.

It is a blessing to be born a man. But because of our state, unless we make a special effort, we cannot enjoy health equal to that of an animal. Thus here too we see the necessity for a health method.

## COMBINING VARIOUS HEALTH METHODS

*Importance of universality in health methods.*   There are only two reasons for a sickly body. Either blood quality is poor, or blood circulation is bad. This is exactly the same as the basic law of economics: production and distribution.

There are two causes of deterioration in the quality of blood: lack of oxygen or insufficient nutrition. When blood circulation becomes sluggish, it is either because the skin function has weakened or because the muscular activity has become dull. There are no other causes for sickness besides these four. Consequently I have divided them into the following four aspects: breathing, diet, skin, and body alignment. Countless health methods have been transmitted according to the Buddhist Yoga way, but when condensed, they boil down to these four items. Again, when one's study broadens to include the health sciences of the world, it becomes complex and divergent, but even then it can be unified under these four headings.

Every health method that has appeared among mankind has its own unique value and we should be grateful, but my one regret is that they are not combined. We have two arms and two legs, and when these four limbs are used, perfect performance is possible. When even one or two are missing, the functional power of the whole breaks down. A destination one can reach in five minutes with two legs will not be reached in ten minutes with one leg. The difference in capability between having one leg or two is not double, but can amount to a differential value of ten or even twenty. This is the "multiplication principle" mentioned earlier. This principle is at work in all phases of man's life, but even an educated man can become forgetful of this important law. When discussing the quality of the blood, many doctors are concerned only with food and say, "You must take more vitamins," but there is hardly one who will say, "You must take in more oxygen." They will say, "You must exercise more" but will hardly teach you the important "You must strengthen your skin." When the body lacks oxygen, no matter how many vitamins you may take, the original power of the vitamins cannot function. Though you may exercise, if you do not look after the skin, your blood circulation will never be sufficient. Similarly, as long as the blood quality is poor, just being concerned with blood circulation is not going to bring good results, and so long as blood circulation is poor, improvement of blood quality will not bring satisfaction. In all things, functioning harmoniously is the important point, just as in physical activities.

Despite the great advances in medicine and health methods throughout the world, there are as yet many sick people. One reason for this state of affairs is lack of a comprehensive synthesis. Therefore, when results are poor, doctors and teachers of health methods should take into consideration this matter of synthesis. Generally, many people make remarks about diet and exercise, but few say anything about breathing or the skin. Because of this proclivity, our health progress is slowed down. That is why I referred especially to "breath, food, skin, and exercise." I sincerely hope readers of this book will remember this and practice the whole synthesis.

*Becoming aware of the principle of the four limbs.* When studying Indian philosophy, one discovers that the "principle of four sides" is strongly emphasized. This is a method where by combining four items, a synthesis is validly manifested. "What does Buddhism teach?" "It teaches the four noble truths," comes the concise answer. The four noble truths are: "Man's life is suffering," "The cause of suffering is a wrong attitude towards life," "This suffering can be dissolved," and "The way to deliverance is to change one's attitude towards life." By this chain of four noble truths, the whole of Buddhism can be expressed completely, so it is in accordance with them that we should examine ourselves. Also, when teaching others, we should always keep in mind these four noble truths. When the four basic truths are taken as the starting point, not only do things proceed more simply, they also proceed without mistakes. Therein lies the value of the "four fundamental truths," a value I have named the "principle of the four limbs."

Four pillars, four-wheeled vehicles, the four great elements: sun, air, water and earth, the four cardinal points: north, south, east, and west—all signify the highest level of stability. Even among animals, those of a higher class all possess four limbs. That it is not three or five but always four must signify the existence of a "supreme balance principle" in the universe. The "principle of four limbs" does not mean the aimless gathering together of four limbs; each has its unique duty and together they help each other. The arm and leg are both limbs, so it might seem that we could exchange their positions, but this would frustrate both arm and leg. The relationship between the left and right limbs is similar. The principle of fourness is unchangeable. So it is with the teaching of the four noble truths. It is not sufficient to put together just any four principles. The four must possess an organic unity.

When studying the organic relation between the four, we become aware that it involves the "three yin-yang principles." "Left hand and right hand," "left foot and right foot," "hands and feet"—in all, three pairs appear, all united by the multiplication principle. Even one multiplication principle manifests a wondrous efficiency, but when three multiplication principles are combined, efficiency will increase all the more. This is what makes the "principle of four limbs" so great. "Breathing and food" is a yin-yang multiplication principle pertaining to the quality of the blood; "skin and exercise" is a yin-yang multiplication principle concerning blood circulation; "breath-food and skin-exercise" is a yin-yang multiplication principle concerned with blood quality and blood circulation; in all, three multiplication principles are established. Three times three equals nine, not six. Nine times nine equals eighty-one, not eighteen. It is this principle of multiplication, not addition, that is utilized in the health method I call the "fourfold unified way."

## THE HEALTH METHOD IN ITSELF AND IN THE PROCESS OF COMMUNICATION

*Unsound life as the cause of illness.* "My good-for-nothing son lost at gambling and came home with a huge debt. This is the second time. He says that unless he pays off the debt within a certain time, his life will be in danger. What shall I do?"

"Did you give him the money the first time?"

"Yes, there was no other way."

"Tell him you'll advance him the money only if he promises to quit gambling."

I am frequently consulted on cases of this kind. Because of differing circumstances, no single answer can be made. At some times, it is better to advance the money, and at others it is better not to. Of course, if the parent keeps advancing money everytime the son comes home with a gambling debt, then the prodigal son will become even more so and will turn into an unhappy man.

Sick people are just like this prodigal son. There is a mistake somewhere in his attitude toward life, so he becomes ill. Man should have faith and practice meditation, but because he does not do so, his breathing becomes shallow and his blood impure. Man should not overeat refined sugar, white bread or meat, but cannot restrain himself and they make his blood impure. Man should make the effort to strengthen his skin, but saying the water is too cold or the climate too cool, he fails to temper the skin and thus corrupts his blood. Man should use his own muscles more, but through overdependence on machines or other people, he putrefies his blood. After all this, if he did not become sick, it would be the eighth wonder of the world.

After becoming sick and going to the doctor, one is told that either surgery or medication will be necessary to get rid of the illness. This is similar to paying off the gambling debts of a prodigal son. Because the patient's attitude was wrong, he became sick, but the doctor does not attempt to correct his attitude. This is like the father who always pays off the prodigal son's gambling debts. He may be considered a kind father for he is saving the son's life, but if this occurs repeatedly, what will be the consequence?

*The right way to go about healing.*    Yoga saw through this, and therefore does not heal imprudently. It has sufficient funds to pay off the prodigal son's debts, but it also knows that at times it is better not to advance him the money. Sickness can be cured through either surgery or medication. But the patient's bad habits are left uncorrected, so where there is a seed, a bud will appear, and he will become sick again. Just as it is necessary to advance money to the prodigal son to save his life for the time being, medical treatment is also necessary. But when this is repeated over and over again, the patient is to be pitied.

In life, appropriateness is needed in many things. But this appropriateness must always be linked to the truth. The Lotus Sutra, which expresses Buddha's real intention, brilliantly expounds the importance of this "appropriateness and truth." Those who adhere to the truth but do not know appropriate means of communicating it will not be able to save others. Still others who stop short with appropriate means of communication but do not know the truth will come to as miserable an end—as the blind man who stumbled off a cliff. I have witnessed the final moment of hundreds of people. Nine out of ten died in misery. I do not mean suicides. Tortured by days of operations and injections, they die in agony. Feeling very saddened I would think, "Why can't they die like men?"

Yoga recognizes the need for surgery and the remedies provided by Western medicine. But this is only after understanding its value as an *appropriate* way. If by any chance we forget the true way, then what was appropriate is not only inappropriate but actually *evil*. The boundary between the appropriate way and the evil way is as thin as a sheet of paper. Everything depends on whether one knows the "truth." A conscientious doctor discerns this. There are many doctors who try to avoid surgery and medication. These good physicians are surely blessed and should enjoy a long and healthy life.


# The Way of Proper Breathing

## UNDERSTANDING THE WAY OF PROPER BREATHING

*Insufficient oxygen as a cause of illness.*    The most important ingredient for our nutrition is not protein or vitamins. It is the oxygen we take in from the air. Hold your nose for one minute and you will understand. Fortunately, twenty percent of the air is oxygen and we can partake of it by merely expanding the lungs. Regardless of the amount of nutrition we may absorb through the mouth, if the oxygen is insufficient, it will not energize the body, just as fire will not burn where there is no air. Western medicine does not seem to be aware of how important oxygen is. As proof, I have never heard of a doctor prescribing, "You must take deeper breaths." High blood pressure is considered one of the hardest-to-cure diseases, but if you practice the breathing method twenty minutes a day, from that very day, your blood pressure will go down, and by continuing it daily you will head toward certain recovery. Even with cancer or heart disease, this breathing method brings great results. These diseases do not have a numerical measuring gauge like the one for high blood pressure, so the results are not visible until several weeks later, but there is no doubt that insufficient oxygen is one of the causes of these two diseases. Many people's hearts beat like a drum when they climb a high mountain. Hold your breath for one minute and then examine the speed of your pulse. The lack of oxygen will cause an instant change in the way your heart works. As stated by Dr. Otto H. Warburg, winner of the Nobel Prize for medicine, cancer must result from the increase of carbon monoxide due to insufficient oxygen.

Called the three great diseases of the civilized world, cancer, heart trouble, and high blood pressure, the chief causes of death still without definite treatment, even these illnesses will clearly improve through the breathing method. How much more so with the simpler diseases? I would go so far as to say that all sickness is always connected with "insufficient oxygen."

*Direct connection between breathing and emotional state.* Blood that flows out of the heart through the artery has a beautiful, clear red color. The blood which returns to the heart after circulating through the body has a bluish muddy color. After one circulation, a time lapse of twenty seconds, the blood color changes swiftly because in delivering oxygen to all the cells, it has gathered carbon dioxide like a city's sanitation department truck. Then the lungs have to feverishly go to work again to purify the impure blood. The heart does not have a day off throughout its whole life, and the lungs too must work twenty-four hours a day without any vacation.

We must understand that because we are human, this important breathing lapses easily into insufficient breathing. Animal parents do not have to worry about saving money for their offsprings' higher education because they have no schools. They do not worry about the hours their children keep because they are not concerned with their children's finding good mates. Man has economic problems as well as family difficulties. In America alone, I understand there are over one million "dropout husbands." A teacher friend told me there are so many fatherless pupils in her classroom that she has stopped using the word "father" in her classroom to avoid hurting some children's feelings. In addition, though present physically, there must be countless husbands who have dropped out mentally. After observing their family life, I can understand why. In Japan, for a long time the male has dominated the female, but in America, it is the opposite, and it is quite understandable why they "evaporate." The women may fume and angrily cry, "Irresponsible" but the human being is weak like a reed.

Because we are men, there is no more end to our worries, our anger, jealousies and hate, than to the summer clouds. No problems would arise if these emotions stayed frozen as emotions, pure and simple, but we are living humans. The winds of emotion instantly become waves of breathing and start to get wild. Emotion and breathing have the same shape as a death mask. When we are worried, our breathing is shallow. When angry, our breathing becomes rough. When we are surprised, power goes into our inhalation, and when relaxed, the exhaling breath becomes long. When in disagreement, we take short breaths, and when in accord we take long, regular breaths.

Emotion and breathing are one. So, for instance, even when we are fearful or angry, if the breathing is controlled and kept tranquil and long, as if nothing had happened, then the emotion will subside. Therefore, the important thing is to prepare ourselves by regularly practicing deep breathing. Through repeated training, physical habits are formed, and in emergencies, the real ability is activated.

Mr. Yuji Iwata teaches the natural instinct way of Yoga. He teaches us how to keep our body relaxed by withdrawing physical power. He told me of a personal experience. One night, while he was walking on a dark street, a shadow suddenly emerged from a side street and pressed a knife against his side. "Give me your money," the robber demanded, and instinctively, Mr. Iwata's body suddenly became soft like jello. The robber must have had some knowledge of the martial arts, for instantly he groveled before Mr. Iwata and bowing profusely begged that his life be spared. "The merits of having a pliable body are great," Mr. Iwata laughed. When unexpectedly threatened with a dagger, it is natural for the body to unconsciously become tense. This is where the daily training pays off. In an emergency, the body reacts by becoming soft. So it is with breathing. If you have undergone daily training, when you are suddenly overwhelmed by a strong emotion of anger or fear, by reflex action, your customary calm breathing will continue, and the violent emotion will even subside.

*Controlling internal organs by will power.*   It will assist you to understand that breathing has the power to control emotions and cure sickness if you understand something of the physiology developed by Yoga masters of the past. The nervous system can be divided into two groups, the conscious nerves and the unconscious nerves, according to the difference in the way they work. The conscious nerves govern the senses whereby we differentiate between hot and cold and they govern the acts of sitting, walking, and the like. The unconscious nerves handle the general internal organs including such functions as heart pulsation and the peristaltic action of the intestines. These work without any effort on our part, so they are also called the autonomic nerves. These autonomic nerves have their center in the midbrain, which is positioned below the cerebrum, and is linked to every organ. There is a reciprocal action among the organs, so when one organ gets out of order, it affects the others; but when one organ is in tiptop condition, the others improve. The name "autonomic" might seem to imply that man can do nothing through will power when a situation calls for correction. But there is one loophole. That is the respiratory function of the lungs.

The lungs are essentially governed by the autonomic nerves and for the most part work unconsciously. Yet at the same time, man can intentionally make his breathing quicker or slower, deeper or shallower. Though there are many organs, it is only in connection with the lungs that the autonomic nerves and conscious nerves can communicate directly. Therein lies the secret of Yoga. For by intentionally practicing lung breathing, a man can unite his autonomic and conscious nerves. Moreover, since the lung's autonomic nerves and those of other organs are connected, we will become able to control the other organs through will power. The yogis of India are a good proof of this fact, and Westerners who have gone to do research on them return home with amazement.

"The yogi was buried under six feet of dirt for a week and he came out alive."

People who hear this cock their heads in disbelief. There are Yoga practitioners who have their bodies bound up with wire, have a weight attached, and sink to the bottom of a river and stay immersed for four hours. Some can swallow pieces of broken glass through the mouth, and five minutes later eject them through the anus; some can suck up a huge amount of water with the anus, while others can take a fatal dosage of poison but excrete it before the system can absorb it. That the key to all these performances lies in breathing can only be called a blessing for mankind.

In this connection, it will be convenient to know a little more about the autonomic nerve. The point to be made here is that the sympathetic and parasympathetic nerves, through a coordinated division of labor, are doing one job. For example, the expansion and contraction of the heart is not the work of just one kind of autonomic nerve. The principle of the seesaw is at work here. The sympathetic nerve contracts and the parasympathetic nerve expands. In general, the sympathetic nerve takes care of the relaxed-type work while the parasympathetic nerve handles the tension-type work. Therefore, as long as these two sets of nerves work in balance, the activity of the inner organs runs smoothly, but when one of them develops a problem then the other will not do its work smoothly and man becomes sick. It is like the two front wheels of an automobile. When they get out of balance, they fall off.

So it is with the lungs, too. The sympathetic and parasympathetic nerves divide the contracting and expanding functions, so when you inhale, inhale fully and when you exhale, exhale completely. Then the balance between your sympathetic and parasympathetic nerves becomes sound, the functions of other organs likewise become balanced, and your ills will be cured. There are over sixty breathing methods in Yoga alone, so when all the other breathing methods, are joined with them, they become countless.

Initially, you may be at a loss to know which one to practice. But through them all flows an undercurrent with four characteristic features: 1. long breath, 2. breath holding, 3. abdominal breathing, and 4. exhaling breath. A long, relaxed breath, holding it, breathing with abdominal movement, and putting power into the exhalation—these are the four. The long breath and holding of the breath are concerned with the "quality of the blood." Abdominal breathing and exhaling are connected with "blood circulation." "Blood quality" and "blood circulation" are part of the yin-yang principle, and supreme health is based on a high level equilibrium between these two, so it is necessary to practice the four, "long, hold, abdomen, exhale," harmoniously. No matter how good the breathing method may be, if mistakenly practiced, the perfection of the yin-yang principle is lost, and the value of the breathing method may be lost. The four items, "long, hold, abdomen, exhale" and its sequence were set up for that very purpose.

## OXYGEN AND EMOTIONAL STABILITY THROUGH DEEP BREATHING—THE LONG BREATH

*Deep breathing as the best way to become beautiful.*   It is generally said, "People who take long breaths have long lives." Yoga says, "A man who takes long breaths *is* long life." When a man takes deep breaths, his whole body receives a sufficient supply of oxygen, his blood is purified, and every one of the fifty trillion cells in his body feel as refreshed as if they had just come out of a bath.

Archbishop Gyosho Fujii is head of the Nippon-zan Myohoji temple and has vowed to build one hundred stupas in honor of Buddha all over the world. A man who attended one of his gatherings once asked me, "The priests and nuns of Nippon-zan have such clear, glowing complexions. Do they use a special cream?" "No, but it's only natural. Correct breathing has merits beyond Zen. Their inhaled breath and exhaled breath is perfectly balanced. Zen practice is a one man wrestling match. At times your mind wanders and your breathing becomes uneven. But with Archbishop Fujii's practice, which is the recitation of the Lotus mantra *Namu myōhō renge kyō*, you could not break the rhythm of the breathing even if you wanted to. It is no wonder you think they all have something on their faces. Every single cell is thoroughly cleansed and sparkling."

I would like to make a suggestion, especially to the ladies. Whenever you think of it, practice long, rhythmical breathing twenty minutes a day, or six times a day divided into three minutes per session, and your complexion will become more beautiful than it could ever become from using expensive cosmetics, and you will glow with a natural charm.

There is no doubting that people who breathe deeply live longer, but the true meaning of long life is not how long you live in calendar years, but how to enjoy the full benefits of deep breathing and long life right now, this instant. The great Zen master, Dozen, who preached "the complete shedding of one's body and mind," died when he was 54 years old, and cannot be considered to have lived to a ripe old age by present-day standards. But with his every thought and every step, he was a practitioner of deep breathing, and can be considered a person who truly attained a long life. Yoga, which advocated that man's happiness or unhappiness is decided by whether man is breathing deeply or shallowly right now, this second, can be said to have grasped the truth of breathing.

*Chief points of the way of deep breathing.*   To practice ideally long breath, mental attitude is naturally important, but also one's physical attitude, prepared by such things as diet, skin care, and body alignment, must be in readiness. These will be elaborated in a later chapter. Right now, I want to instruct you in long breathing.

A.   How to sit: Chair-sitting, Japanese-style sitting or cross-legged sitting is fine. When sitting on a chair, you should not lean against the backrest. When sitting Japanese style, one big toe should be on top of the other, and the knees should be apart a little.

When sitting cross-legged, the heels should touch the abdomen.

B.   The spine must be straight. To do this, pull back the pelvic region, draw back the chin, and stretch up your spinal column.

C.   Arms should not touch the torso. Place your hands on your lap with palms facing up and make a circle with the thumb and index finger while the other three fingers flow out horizontally.

D.   Remaining erect, withdraw all tension. Let first your shoulders, then your arms, neck and head, become soft like custard.

E.   Keep the eyes half open. Choose a focal point one to five yards in front of you, and keep your eyes focused on it at all times while practicing.

F.   Mental sitting. Striving for total harmony of the bodily nerves, focus the mind on the hypogastric region (lower abdomen), the center point of a triangle formed by drawing a line from the navel to the third lumbar vertebrae and thence to the anus. When the mind is focussed there, the whole nervous system cooperates at the highest level.

G.   Two times, at the beginning and end of practice, exhale through the mouth and inhale through the nose, putting special emphasis on the exhalation.

H.   During practice, breathe only with the nose. Inhaling and exhaling must be of same length of time, and when alternating between inhaling and exhaling, it should be smooth like the elliptic motion of a rotary you are unaware of, not jerky like the rectilineal motion of a piston.

I.   Mental attitude. First, consider that the whole body is breathing. The 250 million sweat glands are all breathing simultaneously. Second, when exhaling, recite the Holy Sound "Aum" in your mind or with your voice. Since it will be a long note, it will sound like "Ohmmmm." Third, when you exhale, do it at your own initiative, but when inhaling, feel that Holy Nature is pouring air into you and do it with no sense of effort.

The above is only a brief explanation. Practice at least twenty minutes a day, either all at once or in periods divided according to your convenience.

## BREATH-HOLDING FOR INCREASE OF LUNG CAPACITY AND ABILITY TO CONCENTRATE—THE SUSPENDED BREATH

*Sukh Purvak.*   Suspended breath is something that happens in the breathing process and that everyone has experienced without realizing it. Man's natural breathing seems to be continuous, but actually there are times when he unconsciously stops breathing. When a person is fervently praying, his breathing is always suspended. This is true also when he meets someone he deeply respects. This is because his mind is concentrated.

When one is staring in order to discern an unknown object, or trying to endure pain, the breathing is suspended. That is because the nerves are concentrating. When attempting to activate physical power in an emergency, one suspends breathing. When trying to lift up a heavy object, or pulling back the string of a bow, any movement that requires effort, the breath is suspended unconsciously.

As you can tell from the aforementioned examples, when the physical or mental need for more power arises, suspending the breath does the trick. Yoga gives positive training in suspending the breath and applies it to man's life. Suspended breath is originally a stoppage of breathing. Since it can cause oxygen shortage, a long suspension must be avoided. But by holding the breath as long as possible, increased physical stamina and stronger nerves are attained.

Besides these objectives, suspended breath is practiced at times to increase the lung capacity. Inhale air to the utmost of your capacity and when the lungs reach a point of maximum expansion, hold your breath. Then all the lung cells, which are said to number 50 billion, will be saturated with oxygen and rally to a state of total activity. The chest will also expand. Suspended breath can be practiced anytime, but for the purpose of increasing lung capacity, it should be practiced immediately after full inhalation.

Suspended breath can be practiced together with the long breath method of the previous section, but among the Yoga breathing methods, there is one called Sukh Purvak, which is a wonderful method for awakening the whole nerve system. When long and suspended breathing are combined and practiced in accordance with this method, the results will be most effective.

The essentials of Sukh Purvak (a suspended breath method) are as follows:

A. Sitting position is the same as for long breath.
B. Place the tip of the index finger of the right hand between eyebrows. Lightly press the right nostril with the thumb and exhale through the left nostril.
C. Holding the same position, inhale with left nostril.
D. Lightly press left nostril with the middle and third fingers and suspend breath.
E. Release thumb from right nostril and exhale.
F. In the same position, inhale through right nostril.
G. Press right nostril with thumb and suspend breath.
H. Release middle and third fingers from left nostril and exhale.

Repeat the above process. Ten times is the limit. For beginners, the inhalation, exhalation and suspended breath should each be seven seconds. As you gain skill, try to attain the ratio of 8 seconds: 4 seconds: 16 seconds, training oneself in intense inhaling and suspended breath.
I. Mental attitude. When inhaling, feel that all the inner organs are simultaneously being awakened and the blood circulation becoming invigorated. When exhaling, repeat "Nohmmm" mentally. During suspended breath, free your mind of all thoughts.

This Sukh Purvak is called U breathing in English because the breathing form is similar to that letter. From all the inner organs, tiny microphones are extended to the nostrils. The sudden wind of inhalation passes through the microphones and stimulates the organs, accelerating the awakening of the nerves. The suspended breath follows immediately, so the nerve activity quickly becomes vigorous.

*Explanation of effectiveness of acupuncture.* Since the resumption of relationships between the U.S.A. and the People's Republic of China, and since President Nixon's visit to mainland China, an acupuncture boom has burst on America. "How can diseases be cured just by stimulation with a needle?" "How can afflicted intestinal organs be cured by sticking needles into the leg?" Many doctors are bewildered. There may be doctors even in Japan who are saying the same thing. Yet questions like these show how little Western doctors study. It also proves that they do not know the cause of illnesses. Buddha has reminded us frequently that diseases cannot be cured unless the cause is known. There are only two causes of sickness: poor quality of the blood and bad blood circulation. If there is nothing wrong with the quality, then the circulation must be considered. If the blood circulation is improved, any sickness is curable. Acupuncture stimulates blood circulation.

"How can blood circulation be stimulated by acupuncture?"

"By stimulation with a needle, the nerve connected to an organ is awakened. Stagnant blood circulation means that the nerves are napping. When you shake awake a person who is dozing, he will start working again. In the same way, the needle shakes awake the sleeping nerve."

"But neurologically, there is no connection between the place the needle is inserted and the afflicted organ."

"This connection cannot be discerned by autopsy. A dead body and a living body are completely different. The continued confusion in Western medicine is because their study is based on the dead man, not the whole, living man".

"But medicine is a science, and as long as a neurological connection is not visible, we cannot believe in body points being connected."

"If medicine is a science, then please experiment like a scientist. The principle of wireless transmission of sound by radio is universal knowledge now. Though there is no visible line between the sender and the receiver, they can communicate. Electrical waves are supposed to be invisible, even to a microscope. A body point and an organ communicate like wireless telegraph. Even now as we sit here, countless electrical waves are in action, and countless cosmic waves are intersecting in an intricate pattern. I believe the mutual transmission and reception going on inside the body are highly complex. Yoga perceived this about 3,000 years ago".

American medicine is now on the brink of a great awakening. With a living man as the object of its experiments, it is trying to delve truthfully into the causes of illnesses. It is trying to return to its original state, medicine for the sake of man, not for money. I have been told that the prisons of Denmark became empty and were turned into museums. In the same way, American hospitals may become empty and be turned into museums in the not too distant future. But that does not mean physicians will be unemployed. By then the government will have become wiser and will understand the unlimited necessity for health methods, and ask the doctors to study and propagate preventive medicine. And to the doctors who protect the foundation of man's happiness, the nation will accord the highest respect and pay due compensation.

Experiments in the Yoga health method are being carried on unceasingly, but there is no end. In short, there is no limit to "health." Therefore, there is no limit to the study of health methods. The eternal way of a true physician derives from this fact.

## ABDOMINAL BREATHING FOR IMPROVED BLOOD CIRCULATION AND COOL COURAGE —THE ABDOMINAL BREATH

*Importance of the hypogastric region.* The main purpose of long breathing and suspended breathing is to improve "blood quality," but the purpose of abdominal breathing is to improve "blood circulation." Unlike other animals, man walks in an upright position, so the blood flows downward and has a tendency to accumulate in the legs. But the legs are composed of firm muscles, and with that power are able to chase out the blood. The pelvic region and abdomen do not have the firmness the legs do, so blood coming down from the heart has a tendency to accumulate there. The abdomen is not encircled by any bony framework, enabling it to expand freely. Its balloon-like softness is actually the cause of a problem for man. Because it is soft, the blood easily accumulates there. Blood that should speedily return to the heart cannot do so because of gravity. It is said that half the blood supply of a healthy man remains in the abdomen and two-thirds the blood supply of an unhealthy man.

As the saying goes, "Flowing water never spoils." When the blood becomes stagnant, it rapidly starts to spoil. With a body lying on a battlefield, the hotter the day, the sooner it will start to decompose. After a day has passed, it is unbearable to go near it. This is a very unpleasant example, but it shows what is meant by blood spoiling.

Do not make the mistake of thinking that a dead man and a living man are totally different. Even in a living body, the blood at times stays stagnant in an organ for hours. Because it is still, it starts to rot and cause illness.

"You mean that only the abdominal organs get sick and other organs do not?"

"No, that is not so. Blood that has been stagnating in the abdomen for hours and has started to rot, by some chance will start to circulate through the whole body. But when putrid blood circulates throughout the body, no good can come of it."

Therefore, for the sake of good health, abdominal power becomes necessary. It has been observed that the abdominal power of a sick person is always low. The Yoga of China, *Hsien Tao,* is one step ahead of Indian Yoga on this point. The Japanese word *tanden* ("hypogastric point"), which comes from China, proves this. *Tan* means "healthy blood" and *den* means "field" or source of nutrition. A supply of healthy blood is indeed the best medicine for any affliction. That is why the character for *tan* is used in medicinal names.

We should be grateful to the *Hsien Tao* masters of ancient China for discovering that the abdomen is the "field" (*den*) for making healthy blood. The position of the *tanden* is said to be about 1 1/2 inches below the navel. With this point as the center, exert pressure. The increase of abdominal pressure will enable the large quantity of stagnant blood to get back into its original circulatory track.

In the Japanese Army, officers and men alike wore abdominal belts about three inches wide. Without this belt, it is said there were too many dropouts on a long enforced march. They must have found out the value of the belts through long experience. When a plane makes a sudden dive, a man becomes faint and cannot see well. If, at this instant, pressure is applied to the lower abdomen, one makes a sudden recovery.

How to increase this abdominal power and thus improve blood circulation becomes the problem. Its solution is abdominal breathing. Abdominal breathing is an animal instinct, but since the development of the human brain, man's center of gravity shifted upwards, the abdominal region became a remote outpost, and man adopted a breathing method using only the chest. Abdominal breathing restores the center of gravity to its original abdominal area. Therefore, not only is the blood circulation improved, but the brain becomes sharper, the spirit brightens, movements become quicker, and much good is produced in this manner. This is the fascination of abdominal breathing and the reason for the Oriental expression "a man with stomach."

*Training method for abdominal breathing.* To prepare for abdominal breathing, first do softening manipulations to remove all abdominal stiffness. This is done to facilitate bringing this breathing method to perfection.

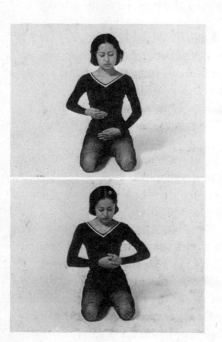

1. Sawing method
Sitting Japanese style, place the left hand on the lower abdomen. With the edge of the little finger of the right hand, press strongly on a line just below the liver, stomach and spleen, and saw back and forth vigorously 30 times. This will remove congested blood from the liver, stomach and spleen and improve blood circulation.

2. Drilling method
Holding the left hand with the right, push the left hand fingertips into the abdomen at a point just below the stomach. Using the left hand middle finger as an axis, drill the finger tips in, rotating back and forth 30 times. When the left hand palm faces right, move the body slightly to the left, and when the palm faces left, move the body to the right. This accelerates blood circulation in the kidney and abdominal aorta.

### 3. Rowing method

Hold the left hand with the right, and loosen the lower abdomen by rubbing up and down. When both hands move downward, both palms face downward. When hands move upward, the palms face up. Do not move hands above the navel, and knead the whole lower abdomen. This removes congested blood from the large and small intestines and invigorates the reproductive organs.

### 4. Arm breathing method

Sit Japanese style. Interlock the fingers and place hands on lower abdomen. As you inhale, gradually raise interlocked hands, timing the ascent so the hands reach the upper chest as you finish inhaling. Gradually lower hands as you exhale so the hands reach the lower abdomen as you finish exhaling.

A. Inhaling

As you inhale, gradually strengthen the power of the *tanden*.

B. Chest press

At the instant you have inhaled to full capacity, press both hands against the upper chest for about one second.

C. Breath emission

The instant you let out a short breath from the nose, ease away your hands and remove pressure from chest for one second. Then immediately enter into suspended breath.

D. Suspended breath

With arms in the same position, add pressure to the *tanden* and push it out in a rolling-up motion until it feels that the navel faces the ceiling. Constrict the rectum. Relax neck and shoulders, but do not disturb abdominal pressure or rectal position. The objective is to attain the highest degree of abdominal power at this time. The length of time it can be sustained depends on the individual's physical condition.

E. Exhaling

With power from the rectum and abdomen, exhale the air. The abdomen will gradually get smaller while still retaining power. It will be easier to practice if you emit a sound while exhaling.

F.   Suspended breath When you have completely exhaled, stop breathing. Keep rectum and abdomen constricted. At this time  congested blood in the abdomen is squeezed out. The length of time will vary depending on the  individual's physical condition. The average is from 5 to 10 seconds.

G.   Resting breath
Suddenly relax abdomen and rectum, and the whole body becomes soft like a ball of cotton. The length of the resting time is optional, but when rested, repeat the whole process (A–G) 5 to 20 times.

*Extraordinary effectiveness of constricting the anus.*   The preceding method of practicing abdominal breathing puts a heavy strain on a beginner, so you should always practice in accordance with your physical condition. It is wise to remember, moreover, that tightening the anus is the secret to correctly attaining abdominal power. Take a drowned man. If his anus is closed, he can be revived. On your death bed, if you need to live a little longer, continuously tighten and release your anus. As long as you have the strength to tighten the anus, you can live. Wills should always be written while still in good health, but some think about the matter only on their death bed. By that time, hands are weak and speech difficult, so it is hard not only for the dying but also for those around him. At such a time, practice the abdominal and rectal method. It should become possible not only to make the will but also to prolong life for two or three days. Some even revive completely and live for many years. Before a parent "drops out" in the face of impending divorce problems, he or she should practice this abdominal breathing. This alone would solve half the problems. Let us protect children from the heartbreak of family break-ups and loneliness.

   Yoga practitioners emphasize the anus. They are able to survive long hours under water because they have "anal power." A long time ago, the Zen priest Enji was crossing Suruga Bay on a ferry when it capsized and all the passengers were lost. A search party was sent out, and the next day a body was found floating among the waves and dragged aboard. The rescuers were expressing sorrow for the poor man's fate when suddenly his eyes opened and he said, "Oh, I am still alive." Priest Enji's anal power must have been well trained through Zen meditation.

   Abdominal breathing does not have to be practiced strictly according to rules. It can be blended with the long breathing. The abdomen can be inflated when inhaling, and squeezed tightly when exhaling. Even this simple method will be effective. As your daily practice progresses, unconsciously your abdomen will be moving and increasing in strength. Even when sleeping, the movement of the abdomen, though covered with blankets, will be noticeable. "Practice makes it yours." That is a blessed law to be thankful for.

## COMPLETE PHYSICAL RELAXATION AND CONTROL OVER ONE'S STATE OF MIND THROUGH EXHALATION—THE EMITTED BREATH

*Through muscular to mental relaxation.* Exhalation too is a breathing method pertaining to blood circulation. In Yoga, it is called *kapalabhati*. I have an uncle who is a teacher of Noh songs. In his thirties, he was afflicted with a severe case of pneumonia and since then has had to be under constant medical care. Even so, he never felt completely healthy. Just as he was beginning to feel he would not be able to live long, he was encouraged to take Noh singing lessons. Since then, he rapidly became stronger, and today, though in his seventies, he is still in the front line of Noh. The next example is that of a friend of mine who was constantly pessimistic because of a chronic stomach disorder. I urged him to take lessons in Chinese poem recitations. He had a very busy schedule, but he started to go to classes regularly, and before long not only his stomach but also his personality made an obvious change for the better. His elated wife thanked me, saying, "My husband has become a better man."

Reciting sutras is one of the practices of Buddhism. It involves straight reading without regard for meaning, so at times it becomes the butt of criticism, but this practice is not altogether meaningless. With loud vocalization, power naturally goes into the exhaled breath, and this is very effective in strengthening the diaphragm and the lung cells. American ministers, like American doctors, have rather short lives, but those in Japan professionally categorized as Buddhist priests have the longest life span of all. When you stop to think about it, Christianity does not have sutra chanting as Buddhism does. They sing psalms, but this is much weaker.

The normal thing is for a troubled man to sigh and for a bored man to yawn. Instinctively, power goes into the "exhaled breath." Stagnant stale air is exhaled, and fresh clean air is poured in. This is because of the principle: the more you exhale, the more you inhale. Yet there is an even more important reason for the breathing methods.

"Now, breathe out," said a nurse giving injections.

"That nurse knows Yoga, too," I said to my daughter who was standing in line next to me. When exhaling, the muscles are relaxed. Yoga exercises were framed to make use of this principle. Yoga exercises give the impression of pliability because of the backing of this exhaling breath.

"Exhaling breath loosens the muscles." The value of this principle is tremendous. This is a principle not only to improve man's health but also to ennoble his character. When the muscles are rigid, even an injection needle cannot penetrate them. The blood flow is then shut off, and not being able to get nutrition, the muscles are ready prey to disease. Let us remember that when the muscles are relaxed, the blood flow is resumed, so the disease is cured. When soaking in a bathtub, we feel relaxed because the muscles slacken and blood circulation becomes active. When your blood pressure becomes critically high, soak in a lukewarm bath. Then for about two hours after getting out, your blood pressure will be lower. Because the muscles relax, the arteries relax. When the arteries relax, blood pressure goes down. Difficult Yoga postures can be done easily inside the bath or soon after a bath.

Man's life is full of tense moments. When the mind becomes tense, the muscles always become tense. When the muscles are tense, the mind next becomes tense. A vicious cycle begins. Today, there is an increase of young people complaining of stiff shoulders. Having a massage after a steam bath makes them feel better, but soon the stiffness returns. Unless they practice relaxing the muscles by themselves, such therapy has no permanent effect.

The stiffness of the muscles is proportionate to the tenseness of the mind. Therefore, when the mind is relaxed, the stiffness of the muscles is also removed. For this purpose, we must never forget the "exhaling breath." Exhale as long and as strongly as possible. If no one is around, laughing loudly is a good device, too. Laughing is an ideal form of exhalation. Let us make an effort to have as many opportunities as possible to laugh loudly. Just as the facial muscles relax, the muscles of the whole body will relax.

*Kapalabhati—How to practice the exhalation method.*
A. The sitting position is the same as for the long breath.
B. Exhaling. Exhale while depressing the abdomen.
C. Inhaling. Expand the abdomen and inhale quickly.
D. Exhaling. Do not suspend breathing, but instantly start to depress the abdomen and exhale decisively.

Do not inhale with a raised chest as if you were surprised. Kapalabhati trains you so lower your diaphragm suddenly. When exhaling, imagine a long waterfall falling straight down, and exhale leisurely but end boldly. With this training, the muscles of the whole body become relaxed, stiffness is washed away, the whole nervous system and the hormone glands become harmonized, and mental concentration is heightened. Repeat five times and stop.

It is not entirely necessary to sit when you practice the exhaling breath method. When you feel the need to release bodily tension, when you feel restless, or if the need arises for mental concentration, practice it two or three times on any occasion. The effect is instantaneous.

So far I have set forth four kinds of breathing methods. Long breath and suspended breath are for blood quality, while abdominal breath and exhaling are for blood circulation. There are countless breathing methods, but all can be resolved into these four. The point is to take in as much oxygen as possible and distribute it well. It must be emphasized that this will not only make our bodies healthier but will improve our brains as well. Oxygen is food for the brain. When oxygen becomes insufficient, the brain stops working before the body does. The reason Buddha placed such high value on the breathing method must be because *satori* ("enlightenment") is directly connected with brain activity.

# The Dietary Way

## Understanding the Dietary Way

*The lesson of the tiered cakes of rice.*   "Food is life" is a teaching typical of Japanese Yoga. The two-tiered rice cake (*kagami mochi*) used in Japan at the New Year season is a good example. It signifies yin and yang and expresses the blessedness of a healthy female body and a healthy male body. It teaches that health is the only starting point from which man can hope for a happy life. How can health be expected? This is symbolized by the bracken, tangerine and sea weed placed on top of the rice cake. Bracken is a very strong wild plant.

I was amazed at its deeprooted tenacity when I went to the snow country of Canada and the tropical land of Hawaii. On both sides of the highways in each country, the bracken was growing profusely, overwhelming the other plants. Its greenness, indicating the preciousness of the life force, must be the reason for its being placed on the rice cake. The tangerine, to put it simply, is the king of vitamins. It not only is especially high in vitamin C but is also a fruit juice acid, which stands as an irreplaceable food. Seaweed is the king of minerals. Though there are countless plants on earth, none supplies such an abundance of minerals as the seaweed.

I have lived in America for over thirty years now and am beginning to forget the life style of Japan, but every New Year I decorate the rice cakes and renew my appreciation of the divine nature.

"By the way, what kind of food do you eat?" I never forget to ask this question when asked to mediate a marital dispute. Unless the couple's bodies are healthy, conjugal love will not continue. It is impossible for children's education or parent's occupation to go smoothly without conjugal affection. Even for a head of state, if his matrimonial relationship is unhappy, he cannot conduct the affairs of state well. Wars between nations occur because domestically unhappy statesmen get together. World peace, so important to all, is based on conjugal love. This discovery is the wisdom of Japanese Yoga. And advancing one step further, Japanese Yoga also discovered the truth that this love is based on physical health—and that this health is based on "healthful food "

*Fasting as the start of true dietetics.* "Food is life" means that the selection of food determines the state of one's health. It means, moreover, that food is the deciding factor of man's fate.

This can be understood when one looks at the saints of the world. Moses of Judaism, Christ of Christianity, Buddha of Buddhism, Muhammad of Islam —all were "practitioners of fasting." Fasting is a religious exercise through which to learn "correct diet." I always urge that every man fast at least once in his lifetime. Unless one masters fasting, the true meaning of diet will never be grasped. Dietetics has developed greatly and physicians are supposed to be the most familiar with it, but these doctors have, on the average, the shortest lives of all.

"Do not ask anxiously, 'What are we to eat? What are we to drink?' " said Jesus. Some Christians get tripped up by this sentence, ignore dietetics, and end up with many diseases and short lives. Jesus was a practitioner of fasting. If there was no food, he could be happy without. Because he was a saint, the words just cited flowed out. People who are in this mental state "naturally refrain from overindulgence" and are able to eat the correct foods in the right amounts. Wild animals do not have dietetics, but in view of the fact that their wisdom regarding food exceeds that of man, the intent of Jesus' words can readily be understood. In short, when man becomes totally one with nature, he can understand true dietetics. Fasting is, indeed, the supreme method to attain oneness with nature.

In the future, too, I believe scientific dietetics will progress. This is one improvement that is greatly to be desired. But the ultimate goal of dietetics is that every man depend only on his own individual instinct for nutrition. Man's physiology itself steadily changes every moment without ceasing. Likewise, man's surroundings are constantly changing. Unless nutritional intake differs in accordance with these changes, we have to do with something that is not true dietetics. A long period of sitting or a long period of activity —these alone should make a big difference in the substance of nutrition. Laughter and anger, these too should change the diet. To put it another way, it is not dietetics that should adapt to this kaleidoscopic condition, but one's self. Fortunately, man also, like the animals, possesses the "instinct" to select naturally the proper food. This "instinct," however, has become contaminated by wrong food habits. We fast to recover it.

Modern dietetics has made rapid progress due to the development of chemistry, but it seems to have an inclination toward the food way taught us by Yoga masters of the past. Yoga is the personal experiment of living men. That modern dietetics is advancing in such a way as to verify this experiment is a happy tendency.

True dietetics, in short, should be based on mankind's thousands of years of experience, to which should be added modern scientific dietetics in a way adapted to every man's instinctive diet. For that purpose, I have listed the four essential elements of the dietary way as follows: prohibited foods, restraint in eating, whole food, and living foods. Not eating food that is poisonous is the meaning of "prohibited foods." "Restraint in eating" means not overeating. "Whole food" means to eat the whole of a product—if a vegetable, the stem, leaves, roots and skin; if a fish, the skin, head, and bones as well "living food" directs us to eat things like raw vegetables, seeds, and nuts. "Prohibited foods" and "restraint in eating" direct us to take precautions so as not to produce toxin within the body. "Whole food" and "living food" teach us to be sure of taking in what is necessary for the body.

## PROHIBITED FOODS

*Priority to non-poisonous rather than nutritious foods.* "It is easy to kill a man with drugs, but difficult to cure him." This is the frightful law of medicine. We spare no effort to give medicine to a patient, but he is not easily cured. Yet it does not take a doctor to kill a man with poison. Anyone can do it quite simply. During the turmoil of World War II, thousands of civilians in Manchuria, Sakhalin and Okinawa are said to have died of potassium cyanide. Swallow it, and everything comes to an end. I understand that the amount needed is no larger than the head of a hatpin.

"It takes months to build and only a minute to break down. How strange!" I heard a carpenter talk thus to himself while wiping his sweating brow. No matter how careful you are about your nutrition, if your care does not include the condition "Never take poison," your dietetics can crumble from the foundation at any time.

"Something is wrong with this dish. Don't eat it," I warned my wife at a wedding reception. The next day I heard that many of the guests at this reception had suffered food poisoning. When animal protein spoils, it is dangerous.

Even a small amount of poison is dangerous. Do not take the risk of thinking a little will not hurt. The recent, tragic death of Mr. Katsuzo Nishi is a sad incident I cannot forget. "I feel so sorry for the black people of America. Just because their skin is black, they are discriminated against. If only there was a way to bleach their skins." Sympathizing with them, he experimented for a long time. Finally, he began to experiment on himself. This experiment involved a chemical that contained arsenic. Just at that time, he received requests for one lecture after another and could not go on a planned fast to eliminate the poison. So it was that he died. Having "died on the battlefront," he must have had no regrets, but it was a great loss to us. Even a master of a splendid health method is powerless against poison.

*A shortage of good politicians?* Preservatives, antidrying chemicals, artificial coloring, insecticides, weed killers, artificial flavoring—all are dangerous.

"Why did you quit your job?", I asked a friend who had worked in a bakery for many years. "Recently they have started to put preservatives and other chemicals into the bread. To do so knowing it is not good for human beings goes against the grain, so I quit."

One day a church member who runs a farm on the outskirts of Sacramento, brought me a crate of vegetables. "Reverend, these vegetables do not have any insecticides on them, so I brought them for you." Unless the farmers use insecticides, the vegetables become infested with bugs, and the markets will not buy them. So, even if reluctantly, they have to use insecticides. There is definitely something wrong with society somewhere. Some people say it is because of crooked politicians. But then we have to ask ourselves who elected those politicians? In the final analysis we have to say that something is wrong with man. That is the reason I am writing this book.

## RESTRAINT IN EATING

*The Buddhist precept of one meal a day.* "All maladies are caused primarily by stagnant food." This is a sentence from the *Nirvana Sutra*. Overeating causes constipation. Constipation leads to autointoxication. Even if you do not take poison from the mouth, you manufacture it within your intestines. Modern medicine knows that this too causes illness.

Buddha left behind many precepts concerning diet. One of them, "One meal a day," is still being practiced by the Theravada Buddhists. If one meal a day is actually practiced, overeating will never occur. "But," some may object, "that may be possible for people who aren't working, but it's impossible for those engaged in heavy labor." It is not so. At one time I did gardening work. It was heavy labor, at times involving the handling of heavy equipment, digging ponds, carrying heavy rocks, etc., but I got by on one meal a day. Dogs romp about happily on one meal a day. I understand they become ill when fed two times or more.

Occasionally you hear the statement, "I put you through college by cutting down from three meals to two." But in older days, it was always two meals a day in Japan. Only in recent years, due to some mistake, it has become three. Two meals a day is nothing out of the ordinary, but modern people are so mistaken in their dietary thinking as to go around publicizing it.

Dr. R. H. Ferguson has stated, "From Hippocrates to this day, all great doctors who have written books on medicine uniformly assert that intestinal stasis is a big cause of sickness and removing it is the secret to cure."

Western medicine and Oriental medicine are completely in accord at least where intestinal stasis is concerned. When waste matter starts adhering to the intestinal walls, it begins to spoil, thus beginning a process that could be called suicide by chronic poisoning. Not only does this toxin flow into the blood stream, but eventually it damages the intestinal walls. That the resultant hypodermal bleeding leads to cerebral hemorrhage is already known. Furthermore, there is a correspondence between the point of hemorrhage in the intestines and the point of hemorrhage in the brain. In fact it may not be entirely accidental that the shape of the intestines and the shape of the brain are somewhat similar.

Those suffering from high blood pressure problems must think of removing the accumulated waste matter. In fact, all people with any kind of illness must clean out their intestines. To do this, not overeating is a major condition. While the waste material still remains, more food is pushed in from the top. It gradually gets harder, sticks to the intestinal walls like toffee, and will not come off easily. First, eliminate what has to be eliminated. This is the point of "restraint in eating."

*Rules for fasting.*    In addition, fasting cannot be forgotten. One meal a day is a kind of fasting, because the stomach is empty longer than it is full. A meal-a-day practitioner does not have to worry about what to eat or drink. Because of his fasting, he will naturally come to eat only foods that are good for him.

For a real fast, I recommend three weeks. But it is very difficult for a beginner to do this at home. Therefore, if you are going to practice it at home, it will be enough to do it only a day or two. Practice for short periods and repeat it as often as you can. I shall state here the most important points to remember when fasting.

1.   During fasting, be steadfast in belief and in a sense of gratitude.
2.   Carry on your regular physical activities during fasting.
3.   Overeating right after fasting is fatal.
4.   Failing to drink as much water as is needed is fatal.
5.   Use the same length of time as was used for fasting to return gradually to a normal diet.

For those for whom fasting is difficult, a raw vegetable diet is recommended. Clean thoroughly over five different kinds of raw vegetables and masticate thoroughly before swallowing. Eat two meals a day. Brown rice powder or brown rice sprouts may be added. In this diet, there is no danger involved when resuming normal diet, and emotionally it is easy to practice.

## WHOLE FOOD

*Four varieties of health food.*    How did man, even though he is an animal, pick up so many mistakes? He generously throws away the best part of the food and eats the remaining "dead" part. The bran and embryo bud of brown rice is cast away, and polished white rice is enjoyed. Potatoes are peeled, cucumbers are peeled, man seems to think vegetables cannot be eaten unless they are peeled.

Due to dietetics, the importance of minerals, vitamins and enzymes has been ascertained, and it is known that they are found most abundantly in the skin or right underneath the skin. In the fish, the skin and bones are the most nutritious, but these are the parts generally accepted as "throw-aways." I have been told that wild bears living on the banks of the Columbia River in Oregon and Washington know when it is the season for salmon to swim upstream and wait to catch them. They eat the head, bones and entrails and leave the flesh. Man does just the opposite.

"Reverend, may I eat beef?"

"Yes, but eat the head first."

This is just a joke, but with vegetables and meat, it is important to eat them wholly. With spinach, the roots should be eaten, too. With carrots, the carrot tops, with cucumbers, the skins and seeds, with fish, the bones and head too. Therefore, I recommend eating small fishes. To eat food in its entirety satisfies the conditions necessary for living. The number of minerals necessary to the human body has already reached the count of fifty and many varieties of vitamins have been discovered. It is impossible to analyze each and every one of them before we eat. Therefore, the most positive way is to eat the "entirety of a living thing." Spinach is leaf and carrots are roots, so they are a good combination, some may think simply and erroneously. Grafting bamboo branches onto a pine tree does not make it a whole. Seeds are small but they are whole. They possess every ingredient necessary to life. Therefore seeds are an "entire food." The embryo bud should of course never be thrown away. To be certain of taking all the nutrition necessary to the human body, it is important to be aware of the entirety of food. All vitamins and minerals work on a mutual compensation basis. Vitamins A and B are important, but cannot work without vitamin C. Potassium and phosphorus are needed, but cannot work without calcium.

I do not encourage any nutritional supplement in the form of pills. They naturally lack something when compared to complete foods. Furthermore, when a certain nutritive becomes excessive it upsets the health of the blood. For example, an overabundance of vitamin A will cause cancer, and excessiveness of B carries with it the danger of making the bones brittle. The hazards of excessiveness are applicable to all medicines. This is the reason for extolling the goodness of "complete foods."

"To begin with, what should I eat?" is a question frequently heard. I hold up four fingers: first, seeds; second, raw vegetables; third, seaweeds; and fourth, small fish. Generally, this should bring you close to a healthful diet. I also teach that at times one should select food that has an abundance of vitamin C which prevents hypodermal bleeding and calcium which prevents acidosis poisoning of the blood. Try it for three weeks. Without doubt, you will notice a visible change in the glow of your complexion and the smoothness of your bowel movements.

For reference, I shall list here some easily available and inexpensive health foods. Foods rich in vitamin C: citrus fruits, persimmon leaf tea, seaweeds, coarse green tea, bell pepper, bean sprouts, spinach, lotus root, cabbage, garlic, onion, white potato, sweet potato, tomato, white radish, carrots, fruits, and vegetables.

Food rich in calcium: milk and milk products, natural grains, beans, nuts, cabbage, carrots, turnip, spinach, pumpkin, sesame, buckwheat, seaweeds, apples, peanuts, citrus fruits.

*Salt-free diet*.   Salt is essential to the body, but Yoga practitioners and wild creatures living in the mountains where there is absolutely no salt available still manage to live quite well. They, too, perspire at times, but still they do not need to take salt. That is because living food, itself, contains sufficient salt. People in general do not notice this, because the sensory power of their tongues has become dull.

When people with high blood pressure go on a salt-free diet, their blood pressure never fails to go down. Experiments involving the heart, kidneys, cancer, stomach ulcers, miscarriages, and obstructions to children's growth prove that salt causes harm. It may be inferred that as long as the heart and stomach do not feel heavy because of lack of salt, the less salt the better. Statistics show salt lovers do not live long.

From ancient days, it has been the custom in Buddhism to abstain from fire and also salt when making supplications to the divinity. The practice was to make a promise like this: "I promise to abstain from salt for twenty-one days, so please grant me my wish." Like fasting and non-use of fire, this was an ascetic practice having to do with the dietary aspect of the way of body and mind.

## LIVING FOOD

*The power of enzymes*.   When food is put into the mouth and masticated for a while, it gradually becomes sweet. That is because the enzyme within the saliva has dissolved the starch elements into sweetness. Protein and fat begin to dissolve in the stomach.

Before this became known, it was thought that stomach action digested the food, but now it is recognized that the action of the enzyme in the gastric juices digests the food. In Hawaii, they rub papaya on tough meat to soften it. Papaya contains an enzyme like that of gastric juices. Fat dropped into tomato juice melts away because tomato contains enzyme elements. Hens incessantly eat sand because mineral elements are needed to make egg shells. They even eat pieces of glass, but it is digested beautifully into egg shells. This too is an enzyme action.

Food is digested and transformed into blood and energy not because of chemical action but because of a living thing: an enzyme. Over a thousand varieties of enzymes are said to have been discovered already, but it is such a tiny living thing that it is difficult for scholars to study. That is a problem for the world of academics, but man, with living wisdom, has made practical use of enzymes since long ago. Soy bean paste, soy sauce, wine and cheese—all were made utilizing the action of enzymes. At our house, we make an enzyme bath using pine needles or rice bran. I heard a very beneficial story from a friend. He had been suffering from corns for years. One day he heard of proteus enzyme and tried it. First, one soaks his feet in warm water for about ten minutes to soften the corn. Then he lightly scrapes the top of the corn with a razor blade, and applies a small amount of strong proteus enzyme (about 10,000 U.S.P. units) and covers with dampened gauze. In my friend's case the corn was gone in the morning. The enzyme ate up the corn.

Minerals and vitamins are important because without them the enzymes become undernourished and cannot function properly. Therefore we must have a sufficient intake of vitamins and minerals, and this is the reason "living food" is important. When raw vegetables and raw green vegetable juice, powdered brown rice and bean sprouts are eaten raw, sufficient vitamins and minerals are absorbed and provide a most propitious menu for the enzymes. Not only papayas and tomatoes but all vegetables have their own beneficial enzyme, but this property is lost in cooking.

There are many reasons for a truth-seeker to go into the mountains, but one is to eat "raw food." Such seekers eat pine needles, nuts, and many other things, the fundamental principle being not to eat any cooked food. These practitioners were called mountain priests in Japan, sages in China, and yogis in India, but their aim was the same—"true health." That modern dietetics is advancing in that direction is good fortune for mankind.

*How to prevent calculous formations.*   At one time, the cartoon "Popeye the Sailorman" was quite popular. When all else failed, he opened a can of spinach, popped it into his mouth, and instantly manifested superhuman power. Spinach contains more vitamins and minerals than other vegetables, which may be the reason it was used in the cartoon, but "canned" spinach is distressing. Only when it is raw is it an invaluable vegetable. Once it is cooked, it not only suffers a drop in nutritional value but actually becomes rather poisonous. The peristaltic movement of the intestines is important in the digestive process, and the motivating power of this peristalsis, the living oxalic acid of the spinach, changes into dead oxalic acid when cooked. Then it unites with the calcium in the blood and causes various calculous symptoms, arthritis, and constipation. By all means let us recognize there is a great difference between raw and cooked vegetables and that "medicine can change into poison."

Generally, raw vegetables contain valuable living oxalic acid, so when you eat raw vegetables, your bowel movement improves. It is important that vegetables not be cooked not only for the sake of this positive result but also to prevent calcium from forming into stones and to help maintain the normal alkaline state of the blood.

*Equilibrium of acid and alkali in the blood.*   The best way to find out the quality of the blood is to determine the proportion of its acid and alkali. A hydrogen ion exponent of 7 indicates a neutral state, but actually, for the blood, 7.2 to 7.4 with a slight inclination toward the alkali is considered the ideal condition. When the blood is in this neutral state, poisonous bacteria cannot increase and one does not become ill from contagious diseases. For the enzymes, this is the optimum condition, enabling them to work well and produce new and good blood. The importance of always maintaining the equilibrium of the blood is to guard against germs and strengthen the enzymes. Fortunately, raw vegetables and whole grains are ideal foods for maintaining this equilibrium. It is said that 90 percent of the sick have acid blood. Partaking large amounts of meat, eggs, refined sugar, and white grains acidifies the blood, so it is advisable to be careful.

"Food without life will not provide life" was the favorite motto of Dr. Kenzo Futaki, a devoted scholar of dietetics who for seventy years experimented with his own body until he passed away in his nineties. The more you study dietetics, the harder it gets. But in the olden days, when the word "dietetics" did not even exist, man was taking in marvelous nutrition. This can easily be understood by observing wild creatures. A neighbor brought home an injured eagle, but it would not eat anything dead. It would not touch even a dead mouse just caught in a trap. It would eat only live ones, so the neighbor, at his wit's end, took it back to the mountain. It is said that an eagle lives two hundred years. Though there are countless living things, the eagle's eyes are said to be sharpest of all. From high up on a cliff, it can see a rat in the valley below.

What about men? They enjoy steaks and roasts, not recognizing the smell of a carcass. I too used to think them delicious before I began to practice fasting. Even the nutritional value of raw vegetables are lost quite rapidly with the passage of time. Fortunately, they do not spoil easily so there is no danger, but they should be eaten while fresh. Onions, carrots, potatoes and yams still remain alive even after being displayed on market stalls so they rank high as health foods even among vegetables. If you think the difference between white rice and brown rice is just in the color, you are greatly mistaken. Not one grain of white rice will sprout, whereas every grain of brown rice will shoot out new green life. White rice begins to spoil and become toxic the instant its life is lost. Brown rice is alive, so it remains unchanged. There are some partially polished brown rices, but they are no good. The reason is simple. They too are dead.

*Unboiled water as a source of nutrition.*   Even drinking water has life in it. Do not kill it before drinking. Let us drink fresh, unboiled water and stop drinking boiled water. Goldfish can not stay alive in cooled, boiled water. Even dwarf trees and plants die. Raw water contains enzymes, oxygen, and minerals, but boiled water does not.

Water is important. When man loses one-tenth of the water within his body, he begins to die. Fasting can be endured for two months, but even five days without water leads to a danger point. Insufficient water causes the growth of a urine poison called guanidine. The dehydration process continues constantly. The daily average is 600 grams from the lungs, 500 grams from the skin, and 1,300 grams from the bladder. The amount of water evaporating from the skin and lungs is about equal to that elimated by the bladder, so we should be aware that we are always dehydrating, whether we realize it or not. Let us drink a glass of water the first thing in the morning, before we move about. While asleep, water was steadily being lost, so the loss must be replenished. Let us keep up the water supply as often as possible. The cells of the body will rejoice in being washed and purified.

"My secret for keeping young is to sip water constantly," an aged but agile lady once told me.

The foregoing explanation of the dietary way can be concluded with the reminder that no matter how nutritious one's diet, no benefit will follow unless he refrains from "prohibited foods," practices "restraint in eating," and remembers to eat "whole foods" and "living foods."

# The Skin Care Way

## UNDERSTANDING THE SKIN CARE WAY

*Importance of excreting toxins.* One can hardly say which is more important: the oxygen that enters through the nose or the food that enters through the mouth. Only when these two work together do they become nourishment for the blood. This is already clear in conventional medicine also, but why is it that many are concerned about food but have never given a moment's thought to breathing? A rope becomes stronger when two strands are entwined together. If the strands were separate, they would be weak. That is why I explained about breathing and diet together. Both are methods for improving the quality of the blood, but at the same time we must also know something about the flow of the blood. "Quality and flow" of the blood—as long as these two are together, all illness should fade away.

The concern with the flow of the blood naturally divides into two parts, the yin and the yang. One is the "Skin Care Way" and the other the "Body Alignment Way." The skin care way is a method of producing blood flow by skin care, and the body alignment way is a means of making the blood flow by alignments of the bones and flesh.

In the Orient, the way of skin care developed in ancient times. In India, there was a group of yogis called the Air-clad Sect, who made it an article of faith to go naked all year round. In China, the discovery of the fourteen meridians emphasized the importance of skin stimulation. In Japan, there was a body purification ceremony, a water austerity that was widespread. The outer forms in these countries were different, but the purpose was the same: "blood circulation."

That stimulation improves blood circulation can be ascertained by the fact that when you scratch the skin, the area gets red, or if you take a bath and thus give the skin a warm stimulant, it again becomes red. This might seem to be nothing but partial reaction, but it is not so. The skin of the whole body is controlled by one nerve system, so even the stimulation of one section results in stimulating the entire skin. Just by warming the hands, one's whole skin is affected and relaxes. Insertion of a needle at one point makes the whole skin shrink. The conductivity of the skin is exceptionally swift. Moreover, stimulation of one part of the skin stimulates the organ connected to that area. When the soles of the feet are rubbed, the kidney is stimulated and its blood circulation improves. When the top of the head is stimulated, the anus becomes tight and washes away bad blood. Altogether three hundred and sixty such points on the skin have been discovered.

A small human egg reaches the uterus and begins to grow, and after three weeks, the construction of the nerve system is begun. At that time, the part that becomes the brain and the part that becomes the skin separate from the same exoderm. Because of this, it must be said that the connection between the brain and the skin is extremely close. If two-thirds of the skin area is covered with paint, breathing becomes difficult, and eventually the brain stops working. When a man is burned over a large portion of his body, his life is endangered because the brain is affected. According to a report made by a committee experimenting on ventilation, if a man is put into a box just large enough to accommodate his body with his head sticking out of the box in touch with fresh air, and stale air is pumped into the box, the man's breathing becomes unbearably difficult. On the contrary, if the body is left out in the fresh air and only the head is stuck into the box of stale air, his breathing does not become difficult. The secret of a clear brain is to keep the skin clean and let it touch fresh air. Because of this principle ,"skin" is given great importance in the Yoga way.

"Nothing is more fearful in this world than a fool." The yogi is aware that this means not others but himself, and so he practices the skin way.

It is said that skin does the work of the lungs. All the sweat glands of the skin, 2,500,000 of them, have their mouths opened toward the outer air. They inhale oxygen and exhale carbon dioxide. The amount of oxygen absorbed is very small, but the amount of carbon dioxide eliminated is great. Carbon monoxide, which is most harmful to the body, is continuously being removed through the skin. Before we think of nutrition, let us first consider the elimination of poison. The excretory action of the skin is indeed great. When the pores of the skin are sealed tightly, man suffers not because of insufficient oxygen, but because the passage of toxin excretion has been stopped.

*How to avoid catching colds.* When a man's body temperature is 98.6°F, he is healthy, but when it gets a degree above or below it, he becomes ill. With the mixture of oxygen and food, calories burn, so inside the body there are physiological actions leading to temperature increase, while outside there is physical action that makes the body temperature climb. In this situation the autonomic nerve system issues an order to the sweat glands to open up and, through perspiration, prevent the body from overheating. When the atmospheric temperature goes down, it closes the sweat glands and even makes goose bumps in its effort to prevent the body temperature from falling. Man is complacent about all this since he is not doing it himself, but for the autonomic nerve system of the skin, it is a continuous job, where not a second of inaction is allowed. "I wish I didn't perspire so much," is the complaint of a careless man.

*Treatment through skin care.* When sickness occurs in an organ, the section of skin related to it always shows some kind of symptom. It can be an itchiness or a fever or a swelling. This symptom can be thought of as a plea from the autonomic system, "This inner organ's blood circulation is poor. Please stimulate it." Ignoring this plea, man pops a poisonous substance, medicine, into his mouth. Fortunately, Oriental medicine was quick to recognize this. Acupuncture, moxa treatment, palm application, finger pressure treatment, massage, hot compress, hot spring cures, and water-shooting treatments were the result.

The brain and skin have a very close connection, but the whole digestive system, which begins at the mouth and ends at the anus, also has a continuous relationship with the skin. When the face gets red, the inner wall of the stomach also gets red. When the face gets pale, the stomach gets pale. The condition of the outer skin is instantly transmitted to the stomach. It seems that the tube from the mouth to the anus can also be considered an extension of the skin. Therefore, when the skin is strengthened, the stomach becomes stronger, and vice versa. Because of this relationship, to make this important digestive organ healthy, the wise thing would be to first strengthen the skin.

Skin is on the outside. You can touch it easily and so can others. For the sake of the skin itself, and also to keep the organs healthy, this must not be forgotten.

I have divided the "Skin Care Way" into four headings: scrubbing, sun bath, hot and cold water bath, and air bath. Focused stimulation through warmth, skin scrubbing and sun bathing bring about good circulation and purification of the blood. Hot and cold water baths and air baths center on stimulation through cold and accelerate the strengthening of the capillaries.

## SCRUBBING THE SKIN

*Ginger massage.* When I was in my teens, I was afflicted with catarrh of the pulmonary apex and pleurisy. At the time, the doctor's diagnosis was that I would not survive to the age of twenty. Both my parents had passed away while I was still a small child and I was raised by my grandparents. They said cold water massage would be good for me. They grated ginger and made ginger tea, then added cold water to make the water massage solution. In Chinese medicine, ginger is used as a cold medicine. Whenever I caught a cold, my grandmother would make me an instant soup consisting of grated ginger, pickled plum, shaved dried bonito, and soy sauce put into a bowl with hot water poured in at the last. If I had a fever, she would go into the garden, dig up three or four worms and simmer them together with a piece of ginger. It is very effective, so even today I encourage others to try it.

Simply scrubbing the skin with cold water is quite beneficial, but when ill, ginger scrubbing is effective. People with weak skin should first disrobe only the upper half of the body, and when finished, dress the upper half and undress the lower. The idea is to stimulate the whole nervous system, so when rubbing, put more stroke power into the direction of the flow of the veins. Generally, the veins flow from both ends towards the center and from the bottom up towards the heart. As an experiment, with the palm of one hand stroke the arm from the wrist towards the heart. You will feel a pleasant sensation, but if you stroke it from the shoulder towards the wrist, the feeling will be uncomfortable.

When you rub one place about twenty times both ways, skin which was first pale will become reddish. By pushing and pulling the blood, the entire blood circulation has suddenly become vigorous. Like polishing copper or silver, you are polishing your body to health. With this thought in mind, continue this practice. If you quit during the scrubbing just because you feel cold, you will catch cold, so do not stop rubbing until you feel the heat radiating. If you still do not feel any heat, then use a kind of brush. Usually, a thin twisted towel should be adequate.

*Following the flow of the veins.* I encourage the practice of scrubbing the whole body with the palms instead of using a towel. For convenience, rubbing only the arms or legs is satisfactory. Though partial, the whole body will be stimulated. At this time too, be sure to rub according to the flow of the veins. Another way of saying this is to rub in the direction opposite to the lie of the bodily hair. Just as the hair on the head all grows downward, so the body hair has a tendency to incline in one direction. By rubbing against it, the massage becomes more effective and the skin more beautiful. Fortunately, I was taught various health methods, the accumulated wisdom of masters of centuries past, by my grandmother. This is not theoretical medicine, but a way to truly save man from his sufferings.

## SUN BATH

*Sunlight for strong teeth.* There is an old Japanese expression, *nenshi,* that normally is used to mean "age" but literally means "teeth age." This is because a man can be judged by the condition of his teeth. If the teeth are strong, man can take in nutrition with good appetite. But there is another more important reason. The teeth represent the bone condition of the whole body. Teeth are a part of the bone family.

The main element in both bones and teeth is calcium. That the teeth weaken when the body is short on calcium is readily proven by the fact that a pregnant woman's teeth are damaged unless she is given extra calcium. In order to grow, the embryo steadily absorbs the calcium of the maternal body, so during this period a pregnant woman must be careful to take in adequate calcium.

It is said that children with weak teeth have small chest girth and weak bone structure. Bow-leggedness is another example, so these children must be given food that is rich in calcium.

"My child is taking sufficient calcium, but still has many cavities. Do you think he is not brushing his teeth thoroughly?"

"I don't think it's the brushing. I think he must be overeating sweets. Sugar is called a pilferer of calcium for it eats away the body calcium. Brushing is not necessary. There even is an old expression, 'teeth as beautiful as a beggars.' Beggars have strong teeth but no affinity for toothbrushes. Natives of the South Pacific do not know of sugar, and of course do not know of tooth brushing, but still have no cavities. Another thing, be sure your child gets sufficient sun. Beggars and natives of the South Pacific docilely accept the blessings of the sun. This is the secret for making strong bones and teeth."

Without vitamin D, calcium cannot become a part of the bone or teeth. When people are out in the sun, vitamin D is compounded in the skin and helps make calcium. Like trees and plants, man cannot remain healthy without the sun. A hospital director once told me that patients in rooms with a southern exposure were discharged sooner than those with a northern exposure. Of the elements of the sun, the ultraviolet ray is the most important, but this is lost when filtered through a glass window, so we must receive the sun's rays directly. Reflected rays are of course the same as "raw sunlight," so if the windows are open in a bright room, we can receive the ultraviolet rays even without going outdoors. Let us choose the sunniest room in the house for a sick member of the family.

*Bone structure and circulatory system.* Blood circulation depends on nerve activity. When those nerves are oppressed, the blood flow is suddenly weakened. Since the nerves run closely along the joints between the bones, when a bone decays like a tooth, the joint deforms and the nerve function becomes incomplete. This is a major cause of sickness. It is readily understood because the instant the joint disorder is treated, the sickness takes a turn for the better. But since the illness itself was the result of weak bones, the bones must be strengthened. A mortician once told me that a man's physical condition at the time of his death is clearly revealed by the weight of his ashes.

"A saint begins his cure by making the bones stronger," said Lao-tse, the father of Chinese Yoga. This means that a true physician will first consider the bones. The common phrases, "bone weary" and "rest the bones" must have been born out of the same feeling as that of Lao-tse.

London is famous for its fog, but I hear that England also has more than its share of hunchbacks. This must be from lack of sunshine. Let us feed more sunshine to the rickets and spinal tuberculosis patients. Crooked bones can be straightened. Even bones that look hard as rocks have blood vessels running through them, and daily regeneration is going on, just as in the skin. All the bones in the body are said to be completely replaced every one and a half years.

My wife raised five children, but she always hung the laundry out in the sun to dry, even though there was a dryer. Babies get diaper rash easily, but if the diapers are dried in the sun, it can be avoided. This is because of the action of the reflected sunlight.

*Sun bath warnings.*    There is no one for whom a sun bath can be harmful, but over-exposure is bad. When sun bathing, always take into consideration your physical condition and the strength of the sun's rays when determining the length and number of exposures. In the case of a sick person, extra care must be taken. First start out with just feet bathing, the next day, up to the knees, and in this manner gradually broaden the area of exposure from the feet upwards. If you have an open, willing spirit, you will be able to tell the amount of exposure best suited to you.

Dr. Takaaki Ohura has experimented widely on calcium. Once he put a rabbit into a cage and left it completely exposed to the sun. For the first thirty minutes, the rabbit seemed content, but after that it started to run around as if trying to find shade. Eventually, it started to bang against the cage until it finally collapsed. During this time, he kept checking the degree of acidity in the blood. During the first thirty minutes it was in a normal alkaline state, but after that it changed to acid. Also, when kept in a dark room, the rabbit's blood changed to acid, but when put into the sun, it returned to alkali. Man has a bigger body than a rabbit, so naturally the length of time differs, too. But this experiment is an important warning. At any rate, the sun makes the bones and the bones make the man. Let us always keep this truth in mind.

## WATER BATHS

*Preventing high blood pressure.*   Keeping the skin clean is an essential condition for strengthening the skin. Because of the clothes we wear, skin excrement clings to it instead of evaporating. The sweat glands become clogged, and skin breathing becomes difficult.

Skin function is weakened, so the brain is also weakened and the organs become sluggish.

"Taking a cold shower is refreshing." This one knows by instinct. The water, with its cold stimulation, invigorates not only the brain, but also the organs, and the whole blood flow is suddenly renovated. Warm water, with its warmth stimulation, relaxes the capillaries and invigorates the blood circulation. Cold and warm, they both affect the circulation, but their process differs greatly.

As you can tell by the skin turning pale, the cold temporarily contracts the capillaries making it difficult for the blood from the artery to pass through. But blood circulation, like the current of a river, cannot reverse its flow, so the blood that has reached the entrance to the capillary seeks a new passageway by which to reach the vein. In 1707, a French anatomist, Lealis Lealis, discovered this secret passage and named it the "glomus." It could be called an "artery and vein intercommunicating tube" and is a kind of capillary situated just this side of the ordinary capillary. When the blood cannot pass into the ordinary capillary, it goes through this intercommunicating tube into the vein. In short, it is similar to the storm drains built to protect cities, and in emergencies blood passes through this tube so the capillary is protected from bursting. But if this tube is clogged, pressure is put only on the capillary, and it bursts. This causes cerebral hemorrhage and also hypodermal bleeding. Therefore, the glomus could be called the safety valve of the blood circulatory system. When you enter a cold bath or shower, the sudden stimulation of the skin contracts the capillaries. At that instant, the glomus opens. Then, according to the physiological principle "what is used develops, what is not used deteriorates," the glomus becomes stronger. That the linking tube is never allowed to become rusty and is always ready to open up is an indispensable condition for a healthy body. The low temperature bath ensures this.

There is another factor hidden in the glomus. By the time the blood that has passed through the capillaries has returned to the veins, it has already distributed all the oxygen and is completely depleted of it, but the blood that goes through the glomus has sufficient oxygen. When this oxygen flows into the vein, the venous tube, which naturally needs the oxygen, revives. There are many diseases related to oxygen deficiency of the venous tubes, such as deafness, gallstones, kidney stones and other stone-forming diseases, and many neurological sicknesses. When there is no oxygen in the blood, the oxalic acid combines with calcium and becomes a calculus. But if the oxygen is there, it will not become a calculus. This is the great mission of the glomus. Therefore, to send blood replete with oxygen to the veins, it is good occasionally to contract the glomus with skin stimulation. The stimulant does not necessarily have to be cold water. During the working day, we often meet with temperature changes outdoors, and also our hands and body touch things thereby receiving contraction stimulation. But alas, man not only wears clothes, but with heaters and coolers he lessens the chance of skin stimulation, and the important glomus withers away. There is no cerebral hemorrhage among animals. The main reason must be that they are constantly in contact with outdoor air.

Consequently, man needs a special skin-tempering practice. The reason sugar and alcohol are bad is that they melt or clog the glomus, and bleeding of the gums and the color of veins showing through the skin are proof of this. Gum bleeding and hypodermal bleeding indicate that the organs are bleeding, too, so unless remedial care is taken, germs can begin to breed and lead to something more serious.

*Cold baths and supernatural power.*  I have personally experienced the cold water austerity 20,000 times. At the age of twenty-five, I was appointed pastor of a church in the cold, northern city of Seattle. In winter the water in the barrel would freeze over two inches thick. One church member, a man named Mr. Moriji Tsubota, was engaged in the steel and pipe business. One day when I visited his home, he said, "I am so grateful. Recently, all the sealed bids I make at auctions have been successful. It is a miracle." Before I could ask him why, he continued, "Reverend, you must do the water austerity. I have been doing it for ten years now. Not only do I not catch cold, I have attained supernatural power. I can tell what is going to happen tomorrow and can also read people's minds."

Incited by this conversation, for thirty-five years I have continuously practiced the cold water bath whenever and wherever possible. At that time I had no knowledge of the glomus, but was drawn to this practice by the traditional Japanese Yoga purification ceremony.

Even plants rejoice when water is sprinkled over their heads. Receiving water through the roots is not sufficient. This reminds me that man's ancestors in the distant past are said to have been fishes, and our nine months in the womb was lived in water, so our biological instincts must be revived when the water touches the skin. At any rate, there is nothing quite like the feeling one experiences after a water austerity. If a water austerity room were prepared in one corner of a company and all the workers were encouraged to take part, absences from sickness should decrease, and with the development of mental alertness, the company fortunes should grow and flourish. As Dr. Katsuzo Nishi claims, "The sixth sense is proportionate to the health of the glomus."

*Secret for recapturing one's youth.*    Warm baths are good for the health. Priest Tenkai, chaplain to three generations of the Tokugawa Shogunate, when he reached the age of 100 was asked by the third Shogun, Iyemitsu, what his secret was for long life. His answer was, "Long life is simple food, honesty, a daily bath, sutra reciting, and occasionally breaking wind." His reply certainly is to the point. The right food, a straightforward mind, clean skin, vigorous recitation of the sutras, and exercise of the hypogastric region. It is said he lived to be 133 years old, carrying on his busy schedule to the end.

I cannot condone using too much soap during baths. The skin is acid, so overuse of an alkali soap must be disturbing to it. A doctor friend said, "Just take a look at my head. Black hair has started to sprout." He stuck his head out for me to see. He was in his seventies and retired. When he was about fifty, he became almost completely bald, and though he never mentioned doctors or medicines, it bothered him. One day, while sitting in a barber shop, he heard a man saying, "A man gets bald because he uses too much soap." At that time he thought nothing of it and soon forgot about it. But several weeks later, at the same barber shop, he heard another man talking, "Old man K. has a new crop of hair on his head. He gives credit to not using soap." This time the doctor could not ignore the matter, and from that day he stopped using shampoo to wash his head.

Three months later, he noticed black fuzz on his head and when I saw him, he had a new crop of fine hair longer than mine, which is a crewcut.

"People should learn from one another."

"Yes, we should."

We were both deeply impressed anew.

A warm bath is especially effective when the blood is acid from overeating meat, eggs, and sugar. The warm bath turns the blood content to alkali. Also, when your blood pressure is up, take a lukewarm bath. The pressure will rapidly go down and leave you out of danger, though only temporarily. When you put pine needles or rice bran into your warm bath, it becomes an enzyme bath, beneficial to the skin and organs. The Japanese people's love for hot springs and water purification must be the greatest in the world, which may be one reason for their gentleness.

When asked the best way of taking a water bath, without hesitation I recommend the following procedure. Line up two bath tubs side by side. Put hot water in one and cold water in the other, and alternate between them, staying in each from thirty seconds to one minute. At the end, always finish with cold water. This is the secret that changes an eighty-year-old man to a forty-year-old youth. Generally, the colder the water the more effective the result, but this too should be decided by consulting your body. According to your physical condition, decide the water temperature. Then gradually decrease the temperature and increase the number of times you alternate from hot to cold. The rule of thumb is three, five, or ten times.

When a child catches cold, I always put him in a cold-hot bath. Children are honest, even sticking their heads under water, so the effect is swift. I feel that one day many American families will provide twin baths in their homes to take cold-hot baths because it is so effective for health, brains, and beauty.

## AIR BATH

*Yoga clothes.*   To wear clothes is unnatural, but this is one point where we cannot return to nature. The next best thing, therefore, is to dress as lightly as possible. Try to avoid undergarments that cling to the body. Allow the air to circulate freely over the skin. Even this much will make you feel much better. That is why I am against belts. It not only cuts off the flow of the air but puts unnatural pressure on the skin. For the same reason I am against neckties. I am not saying that accessories are bad, but binding the neck is. Formerly, a hat was a must for formal occasions, but now it is just a memory of bygone days. A necktie is still required, but even this may fade away. We cannot do away with clothes, but let us avoid whatever constricts the body. It is my hope that the designers will one day come forth with "Yoga clothes," styled so as to avoid constricting the body in any way.

And for bedtime, I recommend sleeping in the nude. Elastic bands are especially bad at night. What need is there for a double layer of briefs and pajamas in bed?

*Nude treatment.*   The great master of modern health method, Dr. Katsuzo Nishi, advocated air bathing. It is especially indispensable to the critically ill because it has power to rejuvenate the heart and can be done without moving the patient. The method is alternately to repeat opening the windows and removing the blankets of the patient, then closing the windows and covering up the patient. Let the time he is uncovered last 20 seconds at first, gradually increasing it to 30 seconds, then 40—adding ten seconds each time. The covered time must always be longer by one minute or two than the nude. Be sure to set the length of time according to the patient's condition. Practice it at least twice a day, and you will discover its worth. The toxins within the body will be excreted through skin stimulation, the liver, kidneys, and stomach will become invigorated, and it will be quite literally an "air bath."

The foregoing has been a brief description of the way of skin care. Scrubbing the skin and the hot-and-cold water baths should be practiced occasionally, but the sun bath and air bath should be practiced all day and every day. This is not to say that one should henceforth spend all his time taking sun baths in the nude. I mean, rather, that the benefits of sun bathing and air bathing should be sought twenty-four hours a day. The benefits of sun bathing are not limited to direct exposure to the sun. By exposing undergarments to the sun and being in rooms with good exposure to the sun, you can receive the benefits of the sun bath even at night. Again, air becomes stale when not in motion, just as water does. Be sure that the air around you is always circulating, whether in your clothes or in your rooms.

# The Body Alignment Way

## UNDERSTANDING THE BODY ALIGNMENT WAY

*Avoiding fatigue.* As in the way of skin care, the prime objective of the body alignment way is to improve the circulation of the blood. The main difference between these two ways is that the former concentrates on the outer skin while the latter focuses on the bones and flesh.

The problem of circulation is essentially a problem of "nerves." When the nerves are restored, blood circulation and health are likewise restored.

If man were still walking on all fours, he might not be plagued by as many diseases as he is now. Because he walks upright, a strain is put on his legs, lumbar, and vertebrae. The legs complain of the heavy body weight, the lumbar protests against the heavy torso, and the vertebrae say the head is too heavy. Because they are forced to support the body weight, the muscles of the leg, lumbar, and spine become tired and stiffen. When the muscles stiffen, they lose their power and cannot support the frame. This causes the dislocation of a joint, but the muscles no longer have the power to correct it. Then the nerve that passes along the joint is put under pressure and blood circulation is impeded. In the beginning it is called fatigue, but later it turns into sickness.

At night when we lie down, muscle tension becomes unnecessary, so we go into an instinctive restoration exercise. First the stiffness goes away, and then the muscles' original "bodily frame adjusting action" begins. Trying to restore the dislocated joint, man tosses around in his sleep. Some people complain of "bad sleeping manners," but this is an important joint-restoring project. Therefore, an older person has good sleeping manners. Some brag, "I wake up in the morning in exactly the same position I fall asleep." But this is nothing to brag about since it only means that he has even lost the power to restore himself. Dislocation itself is not bad. It is not having the power to correct it during sleep that is bad. For this reason I say that the wider and firmer the bed the better, for then you can get your "sleep exercise" more freely.

*Flesh, bone, and the multiplication principle.* Dislocation of the joints is practically non-existent among animals. Their body weight is equally shared by the four limbs, and the frame is easier to balance. Therefore, their sleeping posture must be good, too. If only man could become like the animals, he would have no joint dislocations—or if he did, he would be able to correct them on the spot. The "body alignment way" is the result of learning to make such corrections. This way is divided into two parts, a method to correct the muscles, and a method to adjust the bone frame. True, it is the muscles that get tired, stiffen, and cause dislocation of the body frame. But it also happens that the frame gets out of order, pinches the nerves, and makes the muscles rigid. As in previous descriptions of relationship, the bones and muscles likewise have a yin-yang relationship.

What, then, is the body alignment way? It has four features: the palm-and-fingers method, the swaying-and-vibrating method, the exercise method, and the posture method. The palm-and-fingers method works to soften muscle stiffness, restoring its instinctive power and correcting the bone structure. The swaying-and-vibrating method aims to shake the four limbs or the whole body, accelerating blood circulation and reviving the muscles. The exercise method is to bring the muscles into equilibrium and correct the body frame in such a way as to remove muscle stiffness. The posture method teaches us to always maintain correct posture so as not to put unnecessary burdens on the muscles, and to unite the whole nervous system. The palm-and-fingers method and the swaying-vibrating method focus on the muscles whereas the exercise and posture methods are concerned primarily with the bone structure.

PALM-AND-FINGERS METHOD

*Manual pressure in blood circulation and nutrition.* At the age of ten, I was orphaned and went to a small village near the famous scenic spot Nikko to live with my grandparents and uncle, who were religious people. My grandfather applied moxa and my uncle prac-ticed manual therapy in order to help the villagers. One night a robber entered a nearby home. At that time the master of the house was busy making rope on the earthen floor in the back, and the robber tied him up with the freshly-made rope. The story spread, and the villagers laughed, saying, "He certainly prepared well for that robber." My grand-father then talked to me, "Men are all like him. They are all making ropes to bind them-selves. With the three strands of greed, resentment, and blaming others, they braid the rope and get themselves into a bind. Buddha has taught us the way to unbind that rope. In the sutra, there is a phrase, 'Self-rope, self-bind.' That's the whole thing in a nutshell."

Man's sickness is literally a self-rope and self-bind. He stiffens the sinews of his muscles and binds himself till he becomes sick. Mind and body work on exactly the same principle. The muscle becomes tired because fatigue accumulates there. By driving out the fatigue with manual pressure, the stagnant fatigue element is flushed out along with the blood, and when the pressure of the hand is removed, fresh blood rushes in and cleans and purifies. When neglected, the fatigue element accumulates, finally becomes "stiff" and shrinks. Then the bone is pulled out of place and becomes crooked. When the bone is pulled out of place, the nerve there, like a wrestler pinned down by an opponent, comes under pressure. The nerve becomes paralyzed and causes sickness. When one muscle shrivels, it causes illness in other places because of this reason.

The attractiveness of the palm-and-fingers method is its simplicity. Anyone can do it. But according to one doctor, the outstanding benefit of this method is that four-fifths of the fatigue element, which is lactic acid, resolves itself into glycogen, and returns to its former energy level. It is said that the sages of the Orient survived by eating mist. At any rate, that they remained vigorous and lived a long life may be due in part to the principle of glycogen deoxidation.

For those interested in the palm-and-fingers method, I will point out the fundamentals. If you practice it daily, you will naturally get the hang of it.

1. The thumb, the three center fingers, or the palm will be used depending on the location. Fingers should be straight, not bent. Press with your whole body weight, pressing down slowly and releasing slowly.

2. Repeat pressure on a point three times. Maintain pressure about four seconds each time. For a place like the neck, where the main artery is shallow, shorten the length of time. Palm pressure on the abdominal region should last about ten seconds each time, repeating three to ten times.

3. Learn the vital points once, but later select the points freely, following "divine instinct." If you bind yourself to the formal points, the divine instinct will become dull and make you blind to the true points.

4. You can practice alone, but it is preferable to practice in pairs. Just as there is an attacker and a defender in the art of *kenpō*, so a presser and receiver following this method will gain equally beneficial results. Using the palm and fingers stimulates the brain and eventually affects the whole body.

For beginners, an illustration is given showing the pressure points. Large dots indicate important points.

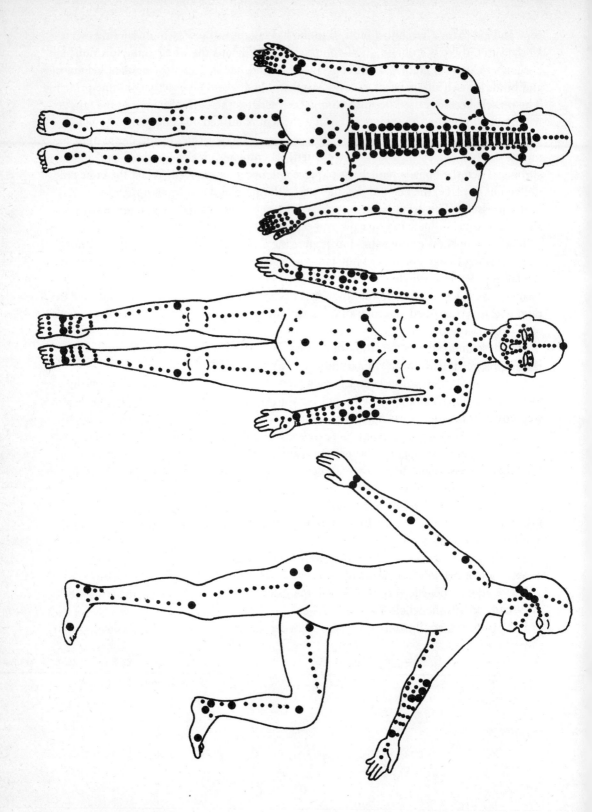

*The "praying hands" position and application of the hands.* They say in Yoga that the hand is a second brain. Beginning with the "praying hands" position, many hand symbols have been transmitted through the ages because a "hand position" has a direct link with one's "inner posture." First make sure each and every finger is in good condition. If there is a weak one, strengthen it by pulling or massaging. When the ten fingers are strong, not only is the brain regulated, but the various inner organs corresponding to it will be stimulated and become stronger. The thumb, mentally, strengthens the will power and, biologically, regulates the respiratory system. The index finger brings forth leadership power and improves the digestive system. The middle finger increases our power of self-examination and adjusts our circulatory system. The ring finger deepens our artistic sense and sharpens the nervous system. The little finger increases the practical sense and energizes the reproductive system.

When you spread out the fingers of both hands as far as you can and touch the tips together in a "fingertip prayer position," pressing the tips strongly against each other, the ten fingers immediately and simultaneously become stronger. While maintaining this position, if you twist the wrists or stretch the arms out in all directions, the result will be doubly effective. To stimulate each finger individually, bend the index and the middle fingers of one hand into fishhook positions, pinch a finger from the other hand between the two, then twist and pull. The ear can be stimulated in this same manner, pinch and pull. The arch of the foot needs strong pressure, so put one thumb on top of the other and press. For the back of the neck and back, slapping with four fingers together is effective. For the head, make a fist and with the little finger side, hit your head all over. If properly performed, this treatment is effective for paraplegics. For aged eyes and nearsightedness, press the fingers around the rims of the eyes and, on the eyeballs, press for a half a minute with the flat of three fingers five times. Good results are bound to follow

Part of the palm-and-fingers method is the practice of "application of the hands." When we feel pain, without even thinking about it our hands go instinctively to the painful spot. This is an expression of divine instinct. "Healing power" radiates from the palm. The rays produced by radium ores cannot be seen, but they possess healing power The curative power of radium springs for skin diseases is wonderful. But radium is a finite and expensive material, whereas everyone has two palms. It would be foolish not to use this convenient "radium ray."

About one hundred years ago, the German anatomist Dr. Meissner ascertained with a microscope that rays were being emitted from the palm. This ray is a kind of enzyme, and every finger is said to have about 50,000 small bodies which can be likened to a cannon shooting off enzyme bullets with a sound. But the amount differs according to the person, and the frequency of discharge changes in accordance with one's emotions. When there is love, discharge frequency is at its greatest. That Buddha's palm is turned out toward the people can be said to be an aspect of his bestowing this enzyme ray. Jesus cured by touching with his hand. In Shinto there is a hand-clapping practice, to purify all with the resounding of this clap. That such a practice exists must be because they acknowledge the special power of the palm. A Grecian holy scripture contains the saying, "Join the hands together, then touch. All diseases will be healed." That the "praying hands" position increases the healing power of the palm can be recognized by the fact that palm healers all over the world are religious people. Joining the hands as if in prayer is not something that grew out of habit, but is a manifestation of instinct. That blood circulation improves after five minutes of joining the hands this way can be proven with a sphygmo-manometer. The lowering of the blood pressure means blood circulation has improved. Assuming the "praying hands" position also sharpens the sensory nerves. Not only do the five senses become keener, but the sixth sense becomes more acute. This way of join-ing the hands also makes the brain function more smoothly because all the nerves of the brain work together more harmoniously. Animals cannot laugh, but man can. I even hear that a "laughing club" was formed to take advantage of this heavenly gift. But joining the hands in prayer is also a godsend, a blessing given only to man. The "praying hands" create health and capability—a good reason for forming a "praying hands club." The Reverend Masaharu Taniguchi, the founder of Seichō-no-Ie, is a pioneer in promoting this practice. No organization in the world applies itself to this practice as his followers do.

For this practice, the finger tips should be level with the top of the head. The fingers must touch each other and be held together without pressure. Be careful that because of this posture the center of balance does not rise higher than the top of the head. Breathe with pressure in the *tanden*. Continue for one to thirty minutes. When applying the hands, it is best to place them back to back with the thumbs crossed and the fingers close together. On occasion it is possible to use only one palm, but in that case the other palm must be held in one of the forms representing the enlightenment of Buddha, and the act is per-formed as an extension of the "praying hands" practice.

## Swaying-and-Vibrating Method

*Hand waving.* The recent advent of massage machines proves, is proof is needed, that vibrating the body improves blood circulation. There are machines to be used during baths, machines said to be especially effective for their whirlpool massage. These are mechanical massage machines, but all of us were born with a massager within our own bodies. Some physical disorders of children cause them to have convulsions. When the body requires heat, it feels chilly and starts to shiver. When a gun is suddenly pointed at you, you can also start shaking. These are actions of the massage machine within you. When better blood circulation is necessary or when the nerves must be aroused into action, the body automatically calls the "instinct of shaking" into action. Yoga developed this natural wisdom into the swaying-and-vibrating method.

In "hand waving" the hands are raised high over the head and shaken, thus forming a sharp contrast to the "seated meditation" of Buddhism. In Shintoism a bell is used in "hand waving" to make its continuance smooth and easier through rhythm, and also for the effect of the sound.

"Hand waving" makes man divine, which means that he receives both physical and mental health. If I tried to explain this in detail, it would take a whole book, so I can only sketch the matter here.

*The heart is not a pump.* We are always told that in order to better one's health, the first thing to consider is the blood circulation. But how can blood circulation be improved? For this an understanding of the structure of the circulatory system becomes necessary. When you understand the structure, you will know how to accelerate it. It is generally accepted that the heart works like a pump. This is, however, the same as to say, "A river flows because it is pushed from the top." The river flows, not because of water pressure from the top, but because of the principle that water is attracted downward. The general medical world does not seem to understand this principle, and so the mistaken common sense view, "the heart is a pump," came into being.

Just think. There are over five billion capillary tubes. The diameter of a tube when contracted is 0.002 ml., when expanded 0.009 ml., and its length is 0.17 ml. How much pressure is necessary to move blood, which has five times the viscosity of water, through this vast number of narrow tubes? The heart is about the size of a fist, its weight about 250 grams, and its pressure about 400 grams. It is a soft lump of muscle.

To pass blood through just one capillary tube would require great pressure, but to pass it through five billion is a job far beyond the capability of the heart. To pass it through with one pump, it is said that a pressure of 100 tons would be necessary. This makes it impossible to accept the heart pump theory. Then what makes blood circulation possible? It is the capillary tubes themselves. This can be proven by physics. A gap of about 0.005 ml. best creates a "capillary phenomenon" and pulls up the water. Water even climbs to the top of the tallest cedar. A cedar tree has a "capillary phenomenon" within it.

Then why does the heart beat? It is not to act as a pump, but to regulate the speed of the circulation. Blood is not water, but is sticky because it contains nutrition. So it has a tendency gradually to adhere to the inner walls of the blood vessels. It is obvious that this will impede the blood flow. The heart temporarily restrains the blood that wants to flow, and according to Hopkin's water current theory, changes the speed of the flow, thereby cleaning off the inner walls of the blood vessels. Therefore, the true function of the heart beat is not to push out the blood, but to curb the blood flow. If the pump's function is to push out the water, then the heart must be called a "dam." The dam's main job is to dam up water, and to let it out when needed. I am sure no one will call a dam device a pump.

*Capillaries as the key to blood circulation.* To improve the circulation of the blood, the first thing to do is to stimulate the capillaries which provide the motive power for blood circulation. Stimulating the heart does not improve blood circulation. On the contrary, it is dangerous. Why is it that bathing improves the circulation? It is not because of stimulation to the heart. It is because the capillary tubes in every nook and corner of the body are stimulated.

The Yoga view is, "When blood circulation is improved, any disease will become better." The ancient practice of hand waving is based on this philosophy. Raising the hands higher than the heart is in itself a factor in improving the circulation as a result of the law of gravity, but in addition, shaking them increases the activity of the capillaries, both neurologically and physically. When the blood in both arms suddenly starts to flow, the blood in the shoulders, neck and head also begins sudden action and eventually accelerates the flow of blood throughout the body. When a cold brings on a sore throat, raise your hands high and shake them for one minute, rest, and repeat ten times. The sore throat will disappear.

*How to practice the swaying-and-vibrating method.*    The man who has most thoroughly studied the principles of blood circulation is Dr. Katsuzo Nishi of Japan. In accordance with the results of his studies he developed and encouraged the practice of four exercises: the "fish exercise," the "capillary exercise," the "clasped hands, clasped feet exercise," and the "back-abdomen exercise."

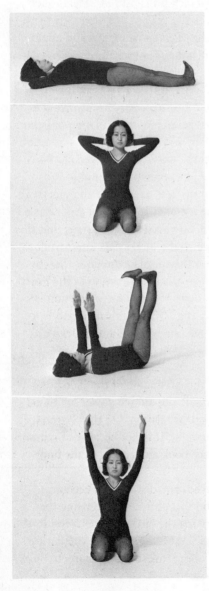

*1.   Fish exercise*
A.   Lie on your back, interlock fingers and place under back of neck. Straighten body, elevate heels and stretch the Achille's tendon. With both arms as your source of power, rhythmically sway them to left and right. The body will curve back and forth like a swimming fish. This corrects dislocated vertebrae. Do continually for 1 to 3 minutes.

B.   During working hours or when there is no space to lie down, this simplified method is recommended. While kneeling, sway the whole upper body from side to side, as in the lying down position. Hands are placed slightly high in back of head. Neck straight.

*2.   Capillary exercise*
A.   Lie on back. Raise arms and legs straight up, perpendicular to the floor. With Achille's tendon stretched tightly, shake all four limbs. Arms and legs contain 75% of the body's capillaries. By stimulating them simultaneously, circulation throughout the entire body is revitalized at once. Shake continuously for at least one minute.

B.   An exercise that can be performed anywhere. Shaking even the arms will improve blood circulation instantly. In case of sore throat, shake for one minute at a time, about 10 times. The higher the hands are raised the better.

### 3. Clasped hands—clasped feet exercise

A. Lie on back. Join palms and bring to chest. Join soles of feet and bring close to buttocks.

B. Stretch clasped hands and feet forcefully and simultaneously. Do not separate clasped hands and feet. Repeat A and B continuously at least 10 times. This corrects imbalance between the right and left sides of the body, and brings symmetry to the whole body. The best exercise for easy childbirth.

### 4. Back-abdomen exercise

A. Sit Japanese style and spread out knees. Place hands on knees and thrust out chest. When body is vertical, abdomen is relaxed.

B. Bend torso right about 40 degrees, then left. When body is inclined, put power into *tanden*, and when vertical, release power. Head and spine must always be in a straight line. Do it 5–10 minutes, progressing till you can repeat 50 times per minute. Effective in balancing the sympathetic and parasympathetic nerves and in maintaining the equilibrium of acidity and alkalinity in the blood. This can be called a speedy method of Zen. It promotes blood circulation in the brain and abdomen. Asthma can also be cured with this exercise.

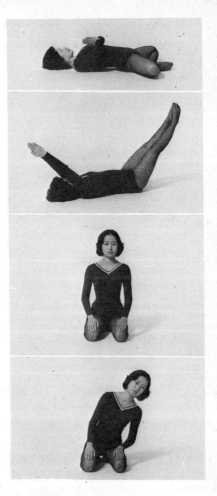

When I was afflicted with pleurisy in my teens, my grandfather used to go out and catch snakes for me to eat. The skin and intestines separate cleanly from the muscular parts. I have seen their spinal columns. They were always lined up in perfect order. In contrast, man's 33 vertebrae run in a zigzag. I believe that a snake remains healthy and can endure the winter's long hibernation because of its strenuous swaying exercise. The fish exercise and the back-abdomen exercise both utilize the principle of the snake.

## ADJUSTING THE BODY THROUGH EXERCISES

*Importance of instinct in exercising.* Yoga exercises can be classified in any number of ways. But they are not done to cure sickness. They are done for perfect posture. When posture is corrected, sickness naturally disappears, just as darkness disappears before light. But correct posture cannot be acquired in a day. If you have been slouching for a long time with your chin sticking out, or if you have long had stiffness in the shoulders and neck, these bad habits adhere to your muscles and bones. You straighten your posture in front of a mirror according to the posture rules, but a minute later, you have returned to your former wrong posture. This is the reason we need not only effort but techniques as well. This is why we need the exercise method.

Take, for example, people with exceptionally stiff shoulders. Mere effort on their part to loosen them will not be effective. The trick of withdrawing stiffness must be learned.

"Ready, put strength into your shoulders. More, more. Now, release it all at once."

This alone should bring relief to the shoulders. This is because "where there is strong concentration, great relaxation follows."

But these ways of exercising are not the product of man's knowledge as we think of it today. You must have seen cats stretching their limbs and dogs briskly shaking their heads. These too are exercises. All animals possess the instinct to correct their posture on the spot whenever they feel a displacement. As an experiment, land a karate chop on a cat's body. Of course, it will be surprised and run away, but at a short distance, it will lie on its back, furiously shake its legs and correct the acute dislocation. Now, if this had been a man, the most he would be capable of is anger. He would not know how to correct the disorder. Just as its instinct is sharp in selecting food, the animal's instinct is sharp for correcting bodily disorders. The Yoga practitioners did not miss this and found that when man's mind became unaffected, sincere, and open, corrective exercises naturally appeared. For many years they experienced this phenomenon, tested it, and finally incorporated it into the Yoga exercises we are endowed with today. I call this "divine culture."

*Sixteen basic exercises.*    The spirit at work in Yoga exercises is indicated in the phrase "instinctive exercises." You "yourself" know best the disorders of your own body. So discover this "self" and under its guidance practice "natural exercises." This is the best Yoga exercise. But Yoga is a middle way. Natural exercises alone are not sufficient, which is the reason various Yoga poses are valued. But it must be clearly understood that these are always "expedients" and not the "True Way."

I have divided Yoga exercises into four steps:
1. Basic exercise
2. Corrective exercise
3. Slow motion exercise
4. Instinctive exercise

There are about 16 basic exercises, refined through 3,000 years of experience. Corrective exercises aim directly at rectifying bad body habits, so one can get into the swing of the basic exercises as quickly as possible. Slow motion exercise puts strength into the muscles through very slow movements. Instinctive exercise means to forget all human contrivances, return to the divinity within us, and exercise according to the natural urge that arises.

In basic exercise, objectives differ according to the pose. Beginners should therefore learn all the poses first, later practicing only those necessary to them. The rules to be observed during practice are as follows:
1. Put power into the hypogastric point (*tanden*).
2. Generally, perform all movements slowly, exhaling during motion.

3.  Concentrate the mind on the muscle and bone that are the focus of the exercise. In exercises involving motion, concentrate in accordance with its progress.
4.  Repeat each exercise twice, and exercise twice a day, in the morning and at night.
5.  Relax after each different pose by lying on your back, all limbs completely released, arms beside the body with palms up.

There are countless Yoga poses. In order to concentrate on what is basic, I have selected the following sixteen, omitting difficult ones, and arranged them in an order that will be easy to follow. Begin with number one and take them consecutively.

The sixteen poses have been divided into four groups of four poses each. After finishing each group, always relax one minute in the relaxation pose. If you practice one group a day, it will not be time consuming.

Yoga is not an ordinary exercise, but a "prayer" practice intended to bring you closer to God, so before you begin your exercises, always sit up straight and clasp your hands in prayer. At the end of the exercises and relaxation pose, again sit up straight and pray. Then proceed to the lotus position and practice breathing. We begin with the sitting and relaxing positions.

*Sitting Poses*
A.   Diamond pose: place one big toe on top of the other. The tips of the thumbs should be close to the forehead.

B.   Lotus pose: place right foot on left thigh, then left foot on right thigh. Place hands on knees, palms up, thumb and second finger of each hand touching to form the letter "O." Stretch the other three fingers straight out.

*Relaxing Poses*
A.   Lying on the back: legs and arms are spread out 30 degrees. Relax the whole body completely. When, in addition, the bones, muscles, internal organs, and brain are also relaxed, the effect of the exercises will be increased twofold.

B.   Lying on the side: using one arm as a pillow, place the hand of the other on the floor. In the same way, let the bottom leg extend straight out from the torso, resting the knee and lower half of the top leg on the floor.

*1.   Knees to stomach pose*
A.   Bring right knee to abdomen and pull down

tightly with the hands for 20 seconds. Stretch right leg and repeat exercise with left.

B.   Bring both knees together to the abdomen and pull down with the hands. (Not recommended for people with high blood pressure.) Beneficial for flatulence, indigestion, improving intestinal tone, and removing face wrinkles.

2.   *Cat pose*
A.   On your hands and knees, with thumbs on the outside, project your abdomen downward and raise head.

B.   Arch your spine as high as you can and pull in abdomen. With thumbs on the inside, lower head and pull chin toward chest. The whole body will become younger and more flexible. Excess fatty deposits in the abdominal area will decrease, improving waist and hip lines.

3.   *Head to knee pose*
A.   Spread out both legs, and bend head forward toward right knee, holding right foot with both hands. Repeat with left leg.

B.   With legs together, bend body forward and touch head to knees, grasping feet with hands. Prevents aging in the legs and improves blood circulation in the rectum and sexual organs.

4.   *Locust pose*
A.   Lie face down with forehead on floor. Make loose fists of hands and place them, palms down, slightly under abdomen. Without bending the knee, raise one leg and hip. Repeat with other leg.

B.   With legs tense and straight, raise both legs together with pelvis. Push fists and chest against floor. Improves function of the heart, liver, and stomach and cures constipation and uterus disorders. Raises and beautifies hips. (Relax one minute.)

5. *Hare pose*

A.   Diamond sitting position: hold heels with hands, place forehead on floor, and stretch neck. Relaxes the spine.

B.   Place forehead on knees, and hold heels with hand. Roll forward to stretch spine, pressing top of head against floor. Stimulates hormone glands in neck and brain. Face and entire body take on youthful appearance. (Can be substituted for headstand.)

6. *Camel pose*

A.   Get down on hands and knees. Stretching arms forward, lower torso until chest touches floor. Helps body become flexible.

B.   Place hands on small of the back. Lean back further and place palms on heels. Push abdomen forward and let head hang back. Beneficial for reproductive and adrenal glands. Beautifies waistline.
(Substitute for arch pose.)

7. *Plow pose*

A.   Stretch Achilles tendons and raise legs to 30 degree angle. Hold this position as long as possible.

B.   Slowly raise legs until feet touch floor behind and as far away as possible from head. Stretches back muscles and brings fresh blood to every section of the vertebrae. Purifies blood congested in lower abdomen. Effective for liver, backaches, and neuralgia. Good for reducing weight.

8. *Bow pose*

A.   Lie on stomach, forehead touching floor. Grasp right ankle with right hand and pull leg up. Repeat with left leg. If one leg seems more difficult to raise than the other, repeat several times with that leg.

B.   Grasp both ankles from the outside, and with knees together, Achilles tendons stretched, and chin and chest pushed out, slowly bring legs and torso up, gradually spreading the knees outward. Corrects

spinal column and increases activity of gonads and kidneys. (Relax one minute.)

9. *Shoulder stand pose*
A.   Lying on floor, slowly raise legs and hips till legs parallel the floor. Stretch arms along floor, palms down, and stretch Achilles tendons. Head and chest should form a 90 degree angle.

B.   Lying on floor face up, raise legs and torso to vertical position, supporting back with both hands. Strengthens thyroid glands, improves flow of blood in liver, and corrects abnormal location or droop of internal organs. One of the best poses for improving natural beauty.

10. *Cobra pose*
A.   Place palms on floor beside chest, elbows bent and touching body, fingertips in line with shoulder. With forehead touching floor, gradually raise the head beginning with the top cervical vertebra and consecutively raise all 24 vertebrae.

B.   From the raised position indicated in the A pose as the starting point, begin with the lowest lumbar vertebrae and slowly lower in order all 24 vertebrae.
   Both A and B poses are improtant. They strengthen the spine and increase its endurance. Beneficial for constipation and feminine diseases.

11. *Spinal twist pose*
A.   Sitting upright, cross right leg over left and rest left elbow on outer side of raised right knee. Repeat in reverse.

B.   Pressing the knee with the elbow, twist your neck and torso to the right. When you have twisted as far as you can go, hold the position briefly, then release all pressure suddenly. Body will return to natural position of its own volition. Repeat from beginning in opposite direction. Stretches and corrects spinal vertebrae and improves blood circulation. Good for neuralgia, inflammations, and displaced internal organs. Develops proper posture.

*12.   Fish pose*
A.   Assume the lotus pose, then lie back. With knees, elbows and top of head pushing against the floor, arch your chest like a bow.

B.   Lift elbows off the floor and stretch to grasp the big toes. Very effective for asthma. Strengthens the lungs, tunes the heart, stimulates intestines and sexual organs. (Relax one minute.)

*13.   Fishhook pose*
A.   Stand erect, holding arms straight out and spreading legs to twice the width of the shoulders.

B.   Keeping knees straight, bend at waist until fingertips of right hand touch outside of right foot. Turn face up and look at left fingertips. Next, bend to the left. Purifies the liver and spleen, corrects constipation and diarrhea, prevents rigidity of abdominal and side muscles, and keeps legs trim.

*14.   Crane pose*
A.   Stand on right foot with left ankle against right thigh. Keep right big toe tense. Cross arms at elbow, bend and interlock fingers leaving index fingers pointing straight up at eye level.

B.   Alternate bending and straightening the right leg. Torso must be vertical at all times. Repeat from beignning with left leg. Balances arms and legs and creates good posture.

*15.   Leg to shoulder pose*
A.   Hook right knee over right arm, bring left arm behind head, and interlock fingers. With the combined power of head and arms, lift leg. Repeat with left knee.

B.   Stretch left leg behind left arm and bring to back of the shoulder. Revives liver and spleen. Strengthens the legs.

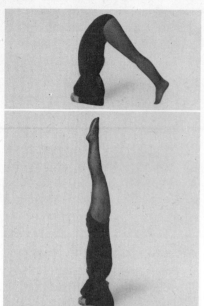

16.  *Headstand pose*
A.  Interlock fingers and place on floor. Put head between both hands; hands placed firmly on head. Draw feet closer towards the head, keeping knees straight. Bring center of gravity to the head, so the feet naturally float upward. (Not recommended for persons with abnormal heart condition or high blood pressure.)

B.  Slowly stretch up legs. This pose is different from others in that you may hold it for a longer period. After assuming the headstand, you can change to other poses, for example the lotus pose. Balances the autonomic nervous system and takes away stiffness from the entire body. Effective for insomnia, nervous irritability. Improves blood circulation to the head and gives tone to the whole body. (Relax one minute.)

The foregoing has been a description of the sixteen basic exercises or poses. Some are more difficult than others and you will not succeed on the first try, but as you continue your efforts, the results will show. The sixteen basic poses can be blended into other poses, according to the person. Under divine guidance, you will devise the poses most suitable to you. And of course as your physical body changes, the poses should be changed, too. Always practice with a sense of gratitude to the masters who have traditionally handed this wisdom down to us for thousands of years. Without gratitude, the results of the basic poses will be nil.

*Corrective exercises.*   After the basic exercises come the corrective ones. Body crookedness differs depending upon the individual. If, at the office, a senior officer is seated to your left, your body will doubtless be twisted to the left. If he sits to your right, your body will be twisted to the right. In games like golf which are one sided, the height of the shoulders tends to become uneven. If a couple always sleeps on the same side of the bed, their bodies will become unbalanced, so they should change positions at times. When climbing stairs, if there is a left curve, the body will develop a left twist as a result of climbing those stairs daily.

"But coming down, the curve is to the right, so won't the body return to normal?"

So it might seem, but the facts are different. Climbing requires power, whereas almost no power is needed for the descent. Consequently, the body develops according to the climb. Various body habits are acquired in accordance with occupation, place, streets used, and even from sickness and personality. A faulty nose causes the chin to jut out, and a bad heart causes the left side of the chest to bulge. Restlessness causes the body to bend forward, and laziness twists the pelvis.

If the posture is truly correct, there should be no fatigue or illness. But life is complex, and various factors lead to posture distortion. Distortion causes fatigue. Fatigue leads to further distortion and thus a vicious cycle develops. Corrective exercises have as their purpose the elimination of this cycle through rectification of bodily habits. Repetition of the basic exercises will gradually correct posture faults, but there are times when more urgent measures become necessary.

As a rule, all exercises should be done by oneself. But essentially man is made to progress through mutual encouragement and help. So reciprocal exercising with two people paired off to correct each other should be encouraged. Corrective exercises can be done alone, but when two people help each other, it not only is easier, but accuracy improves. So, here I will mainly explain the reciprocal corrective exercises. The main points are:

1. Do the basic poses and find out which side of your body is the more rigid. (Usually one is.) If the right is more rigid, take care to put more power into it and repeat exercises more often with the right, and vice versa for the left. In this manner, improve the balance between right and left, and also front and back.

2. Utilize the resisting power of the muscle. For instance, if the pelvis is too tight, sit on the floor, bring both knees to the chest and push with the hands so the knees are brought together, while the knees resist the push. After ten seconds, release the hands from the knees suddenly. The reaction will loosen the pelvis. When the shoulders are stiff, put power into them and relax suddenly. The stiffness will go away. This too is a utilization of the resisting power.

3. Take advantage of the interrelated parts of the body. When the ankle becomes flexible, stiffness in the neck will disappear. When the intestinal blood circulation is accelerated, the flow of blood to the brain is improved. When the rib bones are expanded, the pelvis will expand. When the top of the head is stimulated, the rectum is stimulated. When the right is used a lot, the rigid left becomes more flexible. This interrelationship should be greatly utilized.

4. The sooner body imbalance is corrected, the easier it is to make the correction. So take care to correct imbalance as soon as it happens or is discovered. If you have been sitting for a length of time facing right, immediately twist the body to the left. If you feel your eyes have been overworked, immediately relax your neck. The key is always to diligently correct the imbalance.

5. The physical body differs greatly from a machine in that it possesses a high degree of adaptability. For instance, if the loin should bend towards the right, the spine will bend towards the left, trying to maintain balance. This is all very well, but if it should "harden" like this, it will become the cause of chronic diseases or mental disorders. Therefore, in remedying it, one should seek not a partial but a whole correction. Otherwise body adaptation achieved with no little effort will be destroyed and may even bring bad results.

6. Meditation can be called training for physical balance. If there is even an ounce or a fraction of an inch of imbalance in the body, one cannot actualize the great state of unhindered freedom. Hence the urgent necessity of corrective exercises.

7. When practicing, always maintain power in the *tanden* ("hypogastric point"). Exhale during strenuous movements and inhale during easy ones. When motionless, continue breathing rhythmically for ten or twenty seconds.

8. When muscular equilibrium and balanced bone structure is attained, corrective exercises must not be continued. Thereafter stick to the basic exercises.

Four poses each for the legs, pelvis, spine, shoulders, and neck will be explained in that order. The number of corrective exercises that can be devised is beyond imagining, so I hope readers will take the initiative and continue to experiment.

*Legs*

1. A.  Lying on floor with feet pointing up, turn one foot outwards (away from X) till it forms an angle of 60 degrees with the floor. Repeat with other foot.

B.  Raise one knee and extend other leg. Partner presses down on knee and pelvis at points indicated by O sign. Resisting pressure, try to lift bent knee.

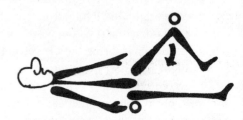

2. A.  Point foot inward (away from X).

B.  Bend the same leg. When partner presses knee down to the floor, resist by spreading legs.

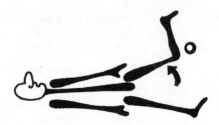

3. A.  Lie on stomach with toes to floor and heels up. Stiffen back muscles of legs.

B.  Have partner stimulate back leg muscles by pressing down with thumb, starting at thigh and working down to ankles.

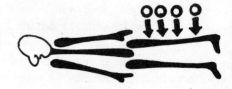

4. A.   Lift foot off floor, bending knee to 90-degree angle. Other party holds heel gently. Try to draw foot to buttocks. Of the two, which leg is weaker?

B.   Have the partner hold the weaker leg and resist strongly.

*Pelvis*

1. A.   Stretch Achilles tendons and raise legs, keeping knees straight. Are heels even, or is one lower than the other?

B.   Hold ankle of one leg with both hands, raising torso and pulling legs toward head while exhaling. Relax when inhaling.

2. A.   Same as 1-A above.

B.   Have partner sit on your buttocks and hold knee of one leg with both hands. As partner gently pulls up, resist by gradually trying to lower the leg.

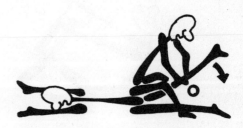

**The Body Alignment Way / 99**

3. A.  Have partner inspect length of legs. One is usually shorter.

B.  Shorter leg remains extended. Bend longer leg. While exhaling, stretch out the extended leg and further bend the bent one.

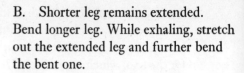

4. A.  Lying on back, try to touch floor with bent knee. Have partner see which shoulder lifts up.

B.  Clasp hands and place behind head. Spread out legs and bend body toward leg on the same side as the shoulder that lifted. Partner pushes down shoulder. Resist.

*Spine*

1. A.  Do the Bow pose. Hold feet from outside. Have partner inspect which way spine is crooked.

B.  Change position of hand to inside on side the spine is bent. Rock body back and forth.

2. A.  Lie on back. Hold palms one inch apart and raise body to 45 degree angle. Have partner see if one arm is shorter than the other.

B.  Stretch shorter arm straight up over head, arm touching ear. Hand of longer arm touches abdomen. Do repeated sit-ups from prone position as partner holds down ankles.

3. A.  Lie on back and raise legs. Have partner tell which leg seems harder to raise.

B.  Partner holds down harder-to-raise leg. Resist and try to raise it.

4. A.  Do the Cobra Pose. Partner tells which leg is shorter.

B.  Raise shorter leg. Bend backward the upper torso on the same side.

*Shoulder*

1. A.  Lie on stomach. Clasp hands behind head and pull back elbows. Partner checks to see which elbow is lower.

B.  Hand of lower elbow is placed behind head. Other hand is placed on hip. Partner holds down feet while you raise body.

2.  A.  Lie on back. Partner inspects nostrils to see which is smaller.

B.  Partner presses down shoulder on the same side as smaller nostril. Resist.

3. A.  Do the Bow Pose and have partner see if neck is straight.

B.  Turn head in opposite direction of neck tilt and rock body back and forth.

4. A.   Stand straight and have partner
see whether one shoulder is higher.
B.   Face downward, lie on floor with
body raised on both arms. Bring hand
of lower shoulder forward, and lower
body by bending elbow. Partner pushes
down gently. Resist.

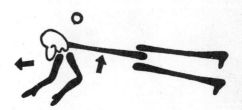

*Neck*

1. A.   Lie on stomach. Rest arm on elbow
and place chin on hands. Partner tells
which elbow is closer to body.

B.   Elbow closer to body is pushed
forward. Partner presses down on back
while you move body up and down.

2. A.   Stand straight. Have partner
inspect which ear is lower.
B.   With heel of palm, hit the head
behind and at the base of the lower
ear.

3. A.  Do the Shoulder stand pose. Partner
tells which way neck is twisted.
B.  Turn neck to the opposite side.
Breathe with Achilles tendons stretched.

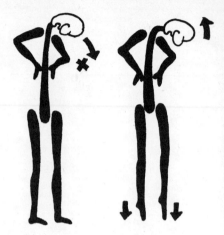

4. A.  Have partner see from behind
which side of neck is swollen.
B.  Lie face down. Have partner hold
down leg on side opposite swelling.
Resist, then have partner release leg
suddenly.

*Joint aligning method.*    The preceding corrective exercises were done with the help of a
partner. The corrective exercises now to be introduced are done completely by the partner. They take about ten minutes. Their purpose is to stimulate all the joints of the body
at the same time, giving particular attention to the sacroiliac, which connects spine and
pelvis.

Man can walk upright because the sacral vertebrae, the lowest vertebrae of the spine,
and the ilium of the pelvis are connected. This sacroiliac is easily thrown out of joint.
In an earlier day doctors thought these were attached and immovable, but Masakichi
Gomi of Japan found after many years of experiments that they become dislocated easily.
And it has been proven that when this dislocation is corrected, the whole body suddenly
revives. Centuries ago, in the Orient, they stressed the importance of maintaining power
in the *tanden,* a point about two inches below the navel. Health was directly connected
with the sacroiliac.

When the sacroiliac gets out of joint, the whole spinal column above it begins to fall out
of joint, causing disorder to all the internal organs as well as impeding the functions of

various organs in the head. This is only natural since the structure has become unbalanced at its foundation. Also, this malalignment directly disturbs the nervous plexus which threads through the sacroiliac, with the result that important organs inside the pelvis and legs fall into a state of paralysis. Dislocation of this pair, the sacrum and the ilium, can progress into a state of total paralysis. Like the rivet of a fan, the sacroiliac can be called the "pivot point of the whole body."

It is marvelous to see how diseases pronounced incurable can in fact be cured just by correcting this joint. In whiplash, too, the sacroiliac must first be corrected for the neck treatment to be effective.

When the pivot point of the whole body, the sacroiliac, is corrected and all the joints of the body are adjusted, then the multiplication process introduced above goes into action and even difficult diseases fade away. This corrective exercise is a preparatory process for practicing meditation. To use it for curing sickness is not its true purpose, but that it can be equally used by the healthy as well as the sick is a great blessing.

Before explaining the joint alignment exercises themselves, it is important that one know how to enter into them.

First, sit up straight, partners facing each other, and with palms together in the "praying hands" position raise hands to eye level and pay respects to each other. This is done also to show appreciation to past masters and to make body and mind pliable and willing. The manipulator must always maintain power in the *tanden* and think that it is not he himself who is doing the manipulating but a "sacred instinct" that guides his movements. When this willing spirit is lacking, it obstructs the emergence of the "sacred instinct" and may even make corrective exercises harmful. The degree of angle, the amount of pressure, etc., will of course differ according to the person and time. The ability to discern this delicate difference depends on the manipulator's sensitive, willing spirit.

The receiver must also be equally relaxed. If he is rigid with fear, the manipulation will not only be ineffective but will become coercive and cause harm. Keep in mind that corrective exercise calls for the perfect teamwork of two persons functioning as one, and complete reliance must be placed in the manipulator.

The manipulator will, at times, use *ki-ai*. *Ki-ai* is a spirited shout uttered just at the moment of going into an important manipulation. Through this, power enters the *tanden* instantaneously, and all the muscles of the manipulator become ideally unified. Simultaneously, the exhaled breath of the *ki-ai* becomes a prayer-like thought that pours into the receiver's body, making the exercise a combination of the mind and body ways.

There are numerous corrective exercises, but I have selected and systematized "sixteen manipulations" which are easy for beginners to learn, and not dangerous. To make them easier to remember, they are numbered and named. The sequence was decided after long experience, and is set up to get the best results in the shortest time.

*1. Pelvis press*
A. Receiver lies down on stomach. Make certain body is straight and see which leg is shorter.

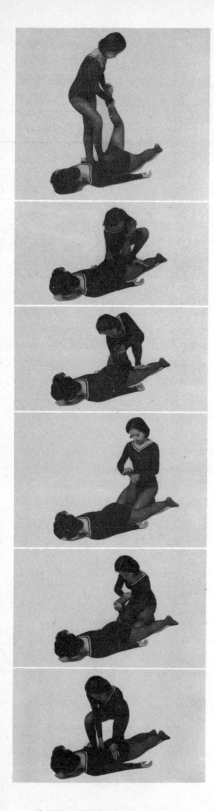

B. With both hands, lift up shorter leg, place heel of foot on the protruding end of ilium. At the instant you press down with heel, emit *ki-ai* and slightly pull leg up.

2. *Knee loosening*
A. Manipulator pushes upper forearm inside back of receiver's knee.

B. Hold ankle with other hand and gently press leg down towards buttock. Manipulator's arm position must not move. Repeat on other leg.

3. *Foot twisting*
A. Manipulator holds receiver's knee between his own, grasps receiver's heel with inside hand and the toes with outer hand, then turns foot to right and left.

B. Turn receiver's foot vigorously to right, left and upward. Make downward pressure gentle, and at lowest point, hold 10 seconds.

4. *Kidney and leg finger-pressure*
A. Press with thumbs on both sides of the spine between the rib and ilium. Each side has 3 points. Put pressure on each for 4 seconds. Repeat.

B. Use finger pressure on back of both legs at 16 points, proceeding from top to bottom. Hold pressure 4 seconds at each point. Repeat.

5. *Neck and shoulder stretch*
A. With receiver's chin on pillow, manipulator places right hand on receiver's left shoulder and left hand on lower back of receiver's head.

B. As if to stretch the line between neck and shoulder, press both hands down and away from each other. Hold 10 seconds at point of maximum stretch.

**6. *Waist twist***
A.   Receiver lies on side. Manipulator places one hand on back of receiver's hip, the other on shoulder of the same side.

B.   Hand on hip pulls forward, hand on shoulder pushes back. Aim is to twist the lumbar vertebrae. Cracking sound from joint is normal. Repeat on other side.

**7. *Thigh pushing***
A.   Receiver lies flat on back. Manipulator, using two hands, lifts up receiver's knee. Upper leg should be vertical.

B.   Manipulator sits astride receiver's knee. With body weight, push down receiver's thigh three times, each time emitting *ki-ai*.

**8. *Making feet firm***
A.   Receiver, lying on back, lifts and bends knee. Manipulator places outside hand over instep as if grasping it. Place other hand on top and, with body weight on hands, press down three times—twice with elasticity and once with *ki-ai*.

B.   Place one hand on receiver's ankle and push down and inward. Place other hand on the receiver's calf just below knee, and with slight elasticity, press inward carefully.

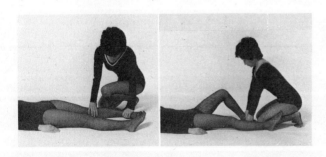

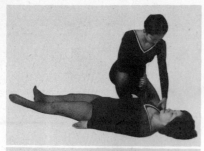

### 9. *Arm and shoulder loosening*
A.  Hold receiver's right elbow with left hand, and his right hand with your right. With his elbow as a pivot, crank hand in such a way as to stimulate shoulder. While slowly twisting arm inward, gently pull elbow. Repeat on left arm.

B.  Press left thumb on receiver's right front shoulder, and with right hand turn his upper right arm 3 times clockwise, counterclockwise 3 times. Repeat on other side.

### 10. *Neck turning*
A.  Manipulator places one hand over other, palms down, and places lower palm on right cheek of receiver. Slowly press and turn neck to extreme point. Hold 10 seconds. Repeat. On third turn, with slight elasticity, push down one inch beyond extreme point. Repeat on left cheek.

B.  Place right hand behind receiver's head with middle finger pressing down outside first cervical vertebra. Place left hand on right cheek. With right hand pulling up and left hand pushing down, turn receiver's neck, stimulating first cervical vertebrae.

### 11. *Pinioning arms*
A.  Receiver interlocks fingers and places hands behind neck. Manipulator threads his arms through receiver's and places hands on top of his.

B.  Pulling receiver's shoulder blades towards his chest with forearms, manipulator arches his body diagonally upward.

## 12. Back pressure

A.   Manipulator squats and places knees against both sides of receiver's lower spine, spreading fingers and placing hands near receiver's stomach.

B.   Manipulator puts top of his head on receiver's back and has him lean back. Putting elastic pressure in knees and hands, gradually move hands and knees upward. The sound of a crack from the joints is normal. Never press knees directly on vertebrae.

## 13. Chest twist

A.   Manipulator places his right knee on receiver's right thigh, his left inner thigh against receiver's buttocks as if to stabilize lower torso. Receiver places right hand on left shoulder, and manipulator puts his left hand over it and his right hand on back of receiver's right shoulder.

B.   With manipulator's chest against receiver's back, together slowly twist upper torso to left. At extreme point of twist, hold 10 seconds and release with force. Relax both knees. Repeat whole process on opposite side.

## 14. Shoulder and neck finger-pressure

A.   Hold receiver's jaw with left hand, and apply manual pressure to his shoulders with right hand. Spread out fingers, and massage and press right and left shoulders simultaneously. The spread between the thumb and index finger should range from the maximum to a minimum of two inches. Press each point 3 times.

B.   Move right hand to the lower back of receiver's head. Pinch the nape with thumb and 4 fingers and massage. Along the border line between neck and cranium, apply manual pressure at the center and 3 points on each side, each point 4 seconds, 2 times. Repeat on opposite side.

## 15. Neck stretching

A.   Support receiver's jaw with left hand, hold nape

with right, and stretch his neck upward.

B.   While neck is still stretched, turn neck to right, then return to frontal position. Repeat 3 times. Repeat whole process on opposite side.

*16.   Hand lifting*
A.   Place both palms on top of receiver's head and recite the mantra *Om-mani-padme-hum* 3 times. Then gradually lower palms, pressing both sides of spine.

B.   Change position of palms so fingers point downward, place palms on sacral vertebra, and repeat mantra 3 times. (After this last exercise, again face each other, assume the "praying hands" position, and bow to one another.)

The foregoing description of the "sixteen manipulations" may seem difficult to understand at first reading. Like swimming or playing the piano, a good teacher plus daily practice is necessary.

Yoga utilizes anything that benefits health. Therefore, acupuncture and moxa are also used. But compared to these corrective exercises, their efficacy is much lower. This is the reason I have systematized the joint-correction exercise into the sixteen manipulations explained here. It should be emphasized again, however, that the health method of Yoga is not a method for curing sicknesses. Unless the body is truly healthy, the mind cannot be truly healthy. If there is even a little stiffness in the body, man cannot attain enlightenment. A fraction of a difference between the right and left, and man cannot become a buddha. Only when the body is completely free of stiffness and imbalance can the mind become completely balanced, lose all stiffness, and attain a "state of godliness." This is the reason for the development of Yoga's austere health method, and the reason Yoga utilizes any method that improves health.

*Slow motion exercises for any occasion.*   Adjusting the body through exercises includes not only the basic and corrective exercises but also the slow motion exercises. Concentrating your strength in the *tanden*, put as much power as possible into all the muscles of the body, and execute one motion very slowly. As in a slow motion movie, you purposely move slowly, but the muscles are strongly tensed. It is most useful to imitate some specific, imagined motion, such as pulling back a bow string, fencing, weight lifting, etc. On the average, 30 seconds is sufficient. If done with great force, limit to 10 seconds. This can be done seated and without attracting the attention of other people, so it can be done even at work when one feels tired. Women should not use too much strength. The muscles might get too bulgy. As long as the motions are done slowly, it will be effective.

*Divine exercise.*   The fourth type of exercise is instinctive exercise. This is the most authentic Yoga exercise. A yawn is an instincitve exercise. Laughing can also be included among the instinctive exercises, since it is not done intentionally but comes out on its own. Therefore, after yawning or laughing, you should feel better.

All living things are given the "instinctive capability" to protect themselves. Animals have no need to study about vitamins and minerals because their instincts lead them to select the necessary nourishment. Man too has been given this instinct, but conceited in his knowledge, he has blinded himself to it. It is generally accepted, now, that children love sweets, but if you place on a tray one glass of milk, one glass of a soft drink, and one glass of green vegetable juice and give the child a choice, a healthy child will always choose green vegetable juice. A carbonated drink has color and is bubbly and sweet, so one would expect it to be the most attractive. Milk too has a close affinity with children, but they do not touch it. Strangely, they reach out for the not too attractive looking vegetable juice. This puts in a new and illuminating perspective the words in the Bible, 'Do not ask anxiously, "What are we to eat? What are we to drink?" '

Green vegetable juice is difficult even for adults to drink, but a child will select it on his own and drink it. The blessedness of instinct brings tears to the eyes. Actually, carbonated drinks and processed milk are not good foods. The natural instinct knows this.

Some parents may say, "But out children love soda and won't drink vegetable juice." The poor children have been victimized by their parents and have lost their instincts. They have been fed refined grains and sugar until their blood has become acidified and toxic. It is no exaggeration to say that their precious instinct has been killed off by poison.

"Instinct" is a word that relates to more than nourishment. It also applies to exercise and thus to blood circulation. When a joint is dislocated, an animal will instantly go into a special motion to adjust it and return it to its former proper position. Of course, the animal does not think out the exercise. His instinct leads him to do it. This instinct is no less than a "god." An infant, after it has been carried on someone's back for a time and is released and put down, will start kicking its feet up and stretching them. This is not just a simple muscle exercise. Being bound by the sash, its vertebrae have become dis-jointed and the exercise is to correct them. During the day, an adult too will scratch himself several times a day. He does not have an insect bite, but somehow he wants to scratch that area. That is because there is an internal disorder in that area. Suddenly, he becomes aware of his unconscious action, and feeling embarrassed, stops scratching. This is bad. Like a cat, he should scratch until satisfied, for this may cure the inner disorder.

"Instinctive exercise" is exercise done completely without conscious intent. It is exer-cise that comes out naturally when the mind submits to the "sacred instinct." If there is anything wrong with the body, instinct will reveal it. When a person without any pre-knowledge of this exercise sees it in action, it may look strange and he may associate it with mental disturbance. But if he is aware that yawning is a natural revelation, then he should be able to easily understand this.

Docilely bow your head before the sacred instinct. Become like a newborn babe. Return to the beginning when there were no ABCs and you only knew how to mouth the nipple. Do not stumble over mistaken views of "infantile mentality." It is a return to the world of no lies. Blessedly, anyone can experience this instinct exercise as long as they become docile.

For practice, a roomy place should be prepared. All dangerous objects and furniture should be removed. It is preferable to have something soft, like a carpet, on the floor. Close your eyes and relax the entire body completely, starting from the head, and proceeding downward through the neck, shoulders, arms, chest, abdomen, hips, and legs. In proportion to the degree of relaxation, the sacred instinct will be manifested. Repeat in your mind, "I have released all power, I have released all conscious intentions, I am completely relaxed." Just as liquid climbs up when you suck a straw, sacred instinct will come pouring in. When you feel like hitting your head, hit it. If you get the urge to bend the neck, bend it. If you get the urge to stretch the legs, stretch them. If you feel like twisting the body, twist. Roll about when you want to. Pound your hips against the floor when you feel like pounding. Do not hesitate to do anything.

The length of time is of no concern. It may be a few minutes or a few hours. Exercise until your eyes open naturally. When your eyes pop open, stop. This is instinct exercise, so no matter how long you do it, you will not feel tired. All phenomenal matters such as where you are or what time it is completely vanish. You forget the time, so when your eyes open, it is normal to be surprised at how much time has gone by.

During the exercise, if the phone rings or someone comes to the door, do not open your eyes suddenly and jump up. With power in your *tanden,* repeat "Thank you" three times, wait for the exercise to come gradually to a halt, quietly open one eye at a time, and stand up. This is the same principle you find in hypnosis.

This instinct exercise is not only directly connected with health, but also with religion. What is God? Even some regular churchgoers are still wondering. Instinctive exercise will solve that question. Though they may have led a religious life for many years, many people lack an experience of God. This exercise is especially recommended for such people. "God really exists"—this first hand experience is, indeed, the key to religion.

*Instinctive exercise and accidents.*    Instinctive exercise is motion that arises without thinking it out in advance. The purer your attitude, the more precise will be the corrective exercise that acts on the afflicted part and causes longstanding disorders to disappear. Everything depends on a person's effort and progress, but instinctive exercise also possesses an unexpected practical value besides that of curing afflictions.

Among today's social problems is that of the "automobile accident." This is the "malignant fear" that it might happen to anyone, anytime. But this fear, too, can be resolved through the principle of instinctive exercise. An accident, by definition, does not occur intentionally. It is all a trick of the "subconscious". When this is understood, you can see how useful the "subconscious training" of instinctive exercise can be. In judo, *kenpō,* piano, or tournaments, at the crucial moment, it is the intensity of the "subconscious" that decides things. It is the experience of sports coaches that learning Yoga cuts down the rate of injuries. That there is a marked difference in piano playing or judo skills after one has learned instinctive exercise can be affirmed by anyone if they will only try it. The aim of instinctive exercise is to bring "unconsciously working power" into play. If the collider, or the one collided with, has both fostered "unconsciously working power," they might have avoided hitting each other.

## POSTURE METHOD

*Posture method as applied to flesh and bone.*   Bad posture can cause illness. Good posture creates health and longevity. An army has various branches. One is (or was) the cavalry. The cavalry was famous for its good posture. Good posture was a must for horseback riding, so soldiers in this branch underwent strict training. It even came to the point where people said, "He must have been in the cavalry. He has such good posture."

Two years of military life ingrained the posture into him, and even after discharge, his posture remained good. This is one reason so many cavalrymen enjoy health and long life.

Correct posture has two aspects: bone structure and muscles. For bone structure, the angle is important, and for muscles, the degree of firmness is important.

The chief points of correct posture as applied to bone structure are:

1.  Both legs are perpendicular, inside lines of legs parallel.
2.  Strongly pull in the pubis.
3.  Stretch spine upward.
4.  Thrust chest out.
5.  Pull chin back.
6.  Left and right shoulders and hips are balanced.
7.  Tip of nose and navel are in a straight line.

The chief points of good posture as applied to the muscles are:

1.  Power is in muscles of big toes.
2.  Achilles tendon is stretched.
3.  Power of hip muscles and abdominal muscles are in balance.
4.  The muscles of the diaphragm, chest, shoulders and neck should be relaxed.
5.  *Tanden* has power and rectum is tightened.

The above has to do with correct carriage for human beings. When this kind of carriage is built up, the muscles of the body feel relaxed and you do not become tired. Fatigue occurs when a muscle is unduly tensed. When all the muscles cooperate and work together, one does not get tired. A friend, who is a fencing teacher, gives a two-hour work-out to his students wearing a hot, heavy protective facial mask, but he shows no sign of fatigue. This is because all his muscles are working evenly. The key is in the words, "Don't hold the sword with your hands. Hold it with your body." A big truck has many tires to support it. No matter how heavy the load may be, the weight is evenly divided, so it can run thousands of miles without difficulty. Our body is so constructed that if all 372 muscles are cooperating, no job should leave us feeling tired. If, despite this, you feel tired, then your posture is incorrect. Instead of all the muscles working in unison, one part is being overworked.

Correct posture is, in short, a "method to unite all muscles." Therefore it can also be called a method of increasing efficiency.

*Causes of neurosis.*   Bad posture invariably makes one tired with a tiredness that affects not only the muscles but also the brain. If you think only with the brain, the brain gets tired. If you think with your whole body, then you do not tire. Neurosis comes from thinking only with the brain. "But," it may be objected, "people have no other way to think. They have to think with the brain." The implication seems to be that they cannot think with the muscles. To this objection my reply is, "The brain is a part of the muscle family, too."

When you pour liquor into the stomach, it is not just the stomach that gets drunk. The feet and brain get drunk as well. Muscle and brain cannot exist separately. When you contemplate things with good posture, the whole body cooperates. To put this in a more easily understandable way, the whole body helps to deal with the fatigue elements that develop in the brain. Even the pores of the skin cooperate to help dispose of fatigue.

*Key to the arts.* Since ancient times, correct posture has been expressed by the single word *tanden*. From the standpoint of physical dynamics, the *tanden* is at the center, but spiritually too, the *tanden* is central. When power is placed in the *tanden*, the whole nervous system is united, and the posture improves naturally. To "do it with the *tanden*" is precisely the same as to "do it with good posture." Sit with the *tanden*, stand with the *tanden*, converse with the *tanden*, read with the *tanden*, hold the broom with the *tanden*, wash dishes with the *tanden*—in all things try to act with spirit and strength in the *tanden*.

You will then discover the truth of the words of past masters, "There is no fatigue when the posture is correct."

Correct posture not only prevents fatigue but is also the key to alertness. The whole body is poised for cooperation, so it naturally acts and reacts speedily. This is the reason fencing teachers maintain power in the *tanden*. Even when driving a car, if people drove with the *tanden* instead of just with their hands, there would be fewer tragic accidents.

Caligraphy teachers also say, "Do not hold the brush with your fingers. Hold it with your *tanden*. Do not manipulate the brush with the fingers. Write with the *tanden*."

Piano, dancing, flower arrangement, tea ceremony, painting or any form of art—unless one enters into them with the *tanden*, there will be no progress.

When the posture improves, character also improves. When a man is too tired, he cannot smile. He will not have the composure to put himself in other people's shoes and think of things from their point of view. That the body feels refreshed is an absolute requirement for being a person of good character.

This explanation of the body alignment way has led to a brief consideration of the palm-and-fingers method, the swaying-and-vibrating method, adjusting the body through exercises, and the posture method. The first two are the "two ways of the muscles" and the latter two the "two ways of the bones." Bones and muscles—these are the key to perfecting the circulation of blood throughout the body.

# 3.   The Way of the Mind

# Necessity for The Way of the Mind

## Meaning of Mental Health

*Being a lamp unto yourself.*  No one walks the streets with his eyes closed. It is too dangerous. But so many are walking the road of life with their eyes closed that it makes one shudder.

"What are you seeking in life?"

"Happiness."

"Where is this happiness?"

"Well . . ."

Without knowing where happiness lies, man is seeking happiness. Suppose one planned to get on a plane going from Los Angeles to Hawaii, asked the Captain "Which way to Hawaii?" and heard him respond, "Uh, well . . ." No one would stay on such a dangerous flight. In a family, the parents are the pilots. Children who must commit themselves to the hands of pilots who do not even know where happiness is, are indeed to be pitied.

In the days before World War II, a Japanese widow in America had a cleaning business. One day, during her absence, the shop caught fire, and when she returned, only smoke and ashes remained. The shock unbalanced her mind, and she was seen walking in circles around the ruins. Three mornings later, she was found dead. She had committed suicide by hanging herself from one of the blackened beams. It was rumored that she had not trusted banks, had cash hidden in the shop, and had followed it to heaven.

The original immigrants suffered great hardship. Without knowledge of English, they had to struggle for survival amidst anti-Japanese feelings. It was only natural, therefore, that her community deeply sympathized with the poor widow's fate. But we must pause here and consider what the mistake was in this widow's life journey that made her die with her money. Though they may not end up as suicides, people who walk life's road without knowing where happiness is are walking a dangerous path.

"Happiness is found only within your mind." These are the words of Buddha who sought and obtained the most sublime happiness. This is the truth of "being a lamp unto yourself." It means that in order to walk safely on the dark road of life, man must make his mind his lamp and depend only on it.

"My husband has no understanding. He has never even held a broom once."

"And who is troubled by this?"

"I am."

"Then you are the one who must change."

The woman herself is the problem, but she mistakenly thinks her husband is the problem. There are many husbands in this world who have never held a broom. But that does not mean their wives are all unhappy. Some are grateful and say, "My husband never meddles in my life." Looking at the same moon, some will rejoice in its beauty, while others will look on it with sad reproach. Man's happiness or unhappiness never exists outside of himself. It exists only within his mind. Unless this truth is grasped, man will suffer forever because of inner poverty. If you want to become happy, you must understand that this happiness has to be sought within your mind. To cultivate the power that will enable you to accept all situations with a feeling of happiness is called "opened eyes."

*Making the truth your only lamp.*   Even though you may understand that "happiness" exists only in your mind, this is still similar to walking with only one eye open. When walking with one eye, it is difficult to judge distances, and this can be dangerous when a car comes by.

"Make the truth your only lamp, and do not depend on other things." This truth is called the "truth lamp." Even after you understand that happiness exists only in your mind, if you do not know what true happiness is, you may have mistaken glass for a diamond. An acquaintance who was rejoicing over a huge ruby he had bought cheaply in Hong Kong, later regretfully said, "Don't buy anything when you go to Hong Kong. That ruby was an imitation." There are true rubies in Hong Kong, but if you do not have eyes to discern, you may return with an imitation.

Even if we possess the jewel of happiness within our minds, we must have eyes to discern the difference between the real and the false. There is in Japan an organization famous for faith-healing through holding the palm close to an afflicted area. A friend, having received its benefits, became a fervent believer and earnestly started to apply the technique to others. In less than six months she herself became seriously ill, far beyond the healing power of even the leaders' palms. She left the organization and told me of the terrors of palm healing. I am not saying this organization was fraudulent. It was her way of understanding that was at fault.

"Happiness is the middle way. The middle way lies between body and mind, between freedom and love. I am a practitioner of the middle way." These are the words of Buddha.

The authentic way is the "middle way." The criterion by which to tell whether a religion is true or false is to see whether it has a proclivity towards the physical or mental, or towards freedom or love. A friend taught me how to appraise sapphires. "Look at this sapphire. This is real because you can see the star. Imitations do not have this star."

Buddha's "happiness appraisal method" was. "Do not choose a religion indiscriminately. Believe only when it is in accord with reason and love."

"We are the chosen people."

"How can you believe that?"

"Only a traitor could ask such a question."

The twenty million souls alive during World War II were victims of the chosen people propaganda.

"Nothing is more fearful than mans' ignorance." This is a Buddhist's watchword.

When man understands these two, the truth of being a lamp unto yourself and the "truth lamp," he can be said to be walking with both eyes open.

## RECOGNIZING WHAT IS UNNATURAL TO THE HUMAN SPIRIT

*You are only human.*   Man is born to walk upright and wear garments. As a result, he is prone to back trouble and skin trouble. This is why we need the Yoga "way of the body."

In the same manner man is by nature an animal that makes too much use of the mind. He has to be frightened, worried, greedy, angry, or repentant. "Has to" admittedly sounds a bit strong, but we must honestly admit that everyone is this way. As a result, the mind starts to warp and everyone's mind becomes more or less unbalanced. This is why we need the Buddhist "way of the mind."

An ignorant man might say, "See how happy I am. I don't need Buddhism." This only proves he is not aware that he was born a man. Cows and birds do not need religion. They do not have to worry about paying taxes on time, not do they aspire to send their children to college. Needless to say, they never repent or feel, "What I did then was bad." There is no reason for these animals to need religion. But man is not an animal. He must go to school, have a wedding service, he even has to worry about his own funeral expenses. It is only natural that he should become filled with complicated worries. And when these are neglected, they turn into insomnia, constipation, alcoholism, chain smoking, lying and scandalmongering. If this is not an "unbalanced mind," what is?

*Non-religious people as mentally unbalanced.*   Man needs a better understanding of his self. Then he will know why religion is necessary to man. Do not become an "intellectual" who steers clear of religion with the excuse, "I know religion is necessary, but I don't like sectarianism, so . . ." If he thinks sectarianism is bad, he should try to get rid of it.

The mentally unbalanced are usually unaware of their own condition. Men are surprisingly frank about their physical disorders and have no hesitation at all about saying, "Doctor, I feel sick. Please take a look at me." But no one goes to him and says, "Doctor, I am insane. Please help me." This is the reason it is so difficult to save the mentally unbalanced.

"Your liver is in bad condition. Take care." His liver has just been denounced, but man is satisfied and almost coolly thinks, "That doctor is a good diagnostician." But if he were to be told, "Your brain is in bad condition; take care," the reaction would be, "How dare he! He called me insane." What a sad commentary on the human condition!

"To save the insane children, I will pretend I am dead, even though I am still alive."

This is a sentence from the Lotus Sutra. The word "insane" appears repeatedly in the sutras. From the standpoint of Buddha's fatherly concern, it must have been literally true that most people were unbalanced.

"Reverend, my head has become funny. Please help me." Just once, when I was in Hawaii, I received that kind of phone call. It was such a rarity that I cannot forget it. I cannot help but pray that all men without religion would be like that. But even with religion, if one becomes entangled with an expedient or exclusive religion, he may become similarly unbalanced.

COMBINING VARIOUS METHODS OF ACHIEVING MENTAL HEALTH

*The non-sectarian nature of Buddhism.*   The greatest flaw of a religious leader is the attitude, "My religion is all-sufficient. There is no need to study other religions." This is one form of mental unbalance. But to become mentally abnormal because of having a religion is too sad for words.

It may be, of course, that it was because he was mentally unbalanced that such a person joined an unbalanced religion. But if, as a result, people were to lose their trust in religion itself, that would be even worse.

"Religion is angelic but sects are satanic." It was the perception of this truth that led Buddha to establish a "religion without sects."

"But why is it that there are so many Buddhist sects? Doesn't this mean Buddhism has assumed a satanic aspect?"

"This is the meaning of the expression 'fruitless study of Buddhism.' This is why people cannot come face to face with Buddha."

"Is there any basis for the claim that Buddhism is nonsectarian?"

"There is, and this may be positively stated. The sutra puts it this way: 'In all times and in all places, whatever is in accord with reason and love belongs to Buddha's teaching.' Expressed as a truth, this takes the form of the principle of non-ego: 'All that is is born as a result of internal causes and external conditions.' When this law is truly understood, it is impossible for sectarianism to exist. Buddha's greatness lay precisely in his discovery of this principle of causation and conditionedness."

In short, any religion, if consistent with reason and beneficial to mankind, is "Buddhism." Today's sects have completely forgotten this vital point, and while serenely pouring sweet tea over the image of the baby Buddha at the annual birthday service, they are actually smearing his face with mud. The expression "insane child" is a sad phrase when applied to self-styled Buddhist disciples, and not to followers of other religions.

*What is hell?* It is amazing that every religion has a merit uniquely its own. Just take this as a fundamental principle and study other religions honestly. You will always discover good points not found in your own. The more you study these good points and make them your own, the more you will eventually help and benefit others, too. This is a way of thinking that no one can deny.

I once heard that the precept "Everyone is my teacher" was the personal ideal of the now deceased eminent Japanese writer, Eiji Yoshikawa. In fact there is nothing wrong with thinking, "All religions are my teachers."

"But wouldn't such a way of thinking weaken my belief?"

"Not in the least. If you learn the good points of other religions, your own religion will grow. I am not saying sectarian ceremonies should be abolished. There are differences between ceremonies, just as there are differences between faces. It is not necessary to make all the same. What counts is its spirit."

"I see. That's comforting."

Even at this level of understanding, this man's faith must have become much deeper. Just at this time, my son had returned from school, saying, "My teacher said hell is where all religious leaders go." Hearing this, I was glad for it showed that man's good sense is still alive. Religious leaders are resolutely attached to sectarianism. There is no sin greater than this, unless it is the sin of doctors. A man kills several persons on the street by shooting wildly. The news appears in big, bold print on the front page of the newspapers. But compared to the crimes committed by doctors and religious leaders, his crime is light.

*Mind quality and flow of mind.*   Many religions profess to "transcend sectarianism." But so far as I have studied them, they all contain a deep sectarianism. You advise members of one religion, "Your religion does not teach this important aspect. Please look into this won't you?" But they remain aloof, impressing you all over again with how sectarian man's spirit is. Because of this, we must always espouse the cause of nonsectarianism, exhorting ourselves and warning others. Unprejudiced and frank, we must study all other religions as we would our own. This is the "way of body and mind."

After studying all kinds of religions, I came to the conclusion that if religion were arranged under four headings, it would be easier for future generations to study. These four headings are: the way of deliverance, the mind-only way, the way of the practice of love, and the way of ascetic training. The way of deliverance studies the law of the universe to gain insight into the real world. In Shintoism this law is called "sincerity," in Buddhism the "pure land," and in Christianity "heaven." What is "heaven"? This has to be discovered on the basis of reason.

The mind-only way has as its goal the creation of this heavenly pure land within this phenomenal world. To do this, it is essential to know what is meant by "mind."

The way of the practice of love is the way of humanity, compassion, and love. It is the way to acquire true self-blessing through the practice of kindness.

The way of ascetic training is the way of prayer, Zen, worship, and physical purification. It aims to make people authentically virtuous and charitable through the training of body and mind.

The first and second are concerned with inner attitude, the third and fourth with stipulations for its practice. In a word, the former has to do with intelligence, the latter with practice.

"Intelligence is like the eye, and practice like the legs," is Buddha's definition. It means there is no "wisdom" that surpasses deliverance and mind-only, and no "practice" greater than the practice of love and self-training.

These four may properly be correlated with the preceding four headings in the way of the body. Just as breathing and diet were connected with the quality of the blood, and skin and body alignment with blood circulation, deliverance and mind-only have an influence on the quality of the mind, and the practice of love and self-training influence the action of the mind. Deliverance and mind-only are absorbed by the mind as its nutrition. Practicing love and training the self bring about a flow of mind whereby they are actualized in all of life. Therefore, I have ventured to coin the expressions "quality of mind" and "flow of mind." The ultimate of physical health is "blood quality and blood circulation." The sum total of mental health is "mind quality and flow of mind."

A complete "way of the mind" must be endowed with all four provisions; deliverance, mind-only, the practice of love, and self-training. If even one were missing, the other three would become weak in accordance with the multiplication principle. Take the four limbs. If one were lacking, the other three could not help being weakened in total effectiveness. The same principle is at work here. Though there are countless sects in the world,

I have yet to see one that is completely endowed with these four. This is the reason for the weakness of the sects themselves, and the reason religious culture is treated so lightly.

## THE WAY OF THE MIND IN ITSELF AND IN THE PROCESS OF COMMUNICATION

*Religious sects as temporary expedients.*   Surprising differences exist among people as regards their state of mind. When the benefits of Yoga exercises are explained, one man will say, "I am too old now for exercises, "whereas another will say, "I am old, so now I must start exercising before I get any older." It is useless to talk about exercising to someone who hates to exercise. "Methodical breathing is really good. If you breathe deeply just three times, your blood pressure will go down 5 ml." This exercise-hater may think, "I have to breathe anyway, so I might as well give it a try."

He practices it, and sure enough his blood pressure goes down. Not only blood pressure, but his bowel movements improve. Naturally this man becomes a practitioner of methodical breathing and his general physical condition improves. At this point he may be ready for a new approach. "Exercise is really good. It helps you stay young." "What kinds of exercises?" In this manner, he may be gradually led into real Yoga. It is the same with religion. Man does not necessarily prefer the true way nor is there any guarantee that he will understand it. Therefore, in order to save man, expedients are used.

"Does Santa Claus really come in through the chimney?"

"Yes, if you are a good child, he will bring you a nice present."

This is an "expedient," not a "falsehood." In this world, there are people who give to others without any strings attached, people who have boundless love for a child's pure mind, and appreciate the hardships of a saint. All these religious truths are taught by Santa Claus. When a child gets older, he realizes there is actually no such human being as Santa and he loses interest in hanging up stockings by the fireplace, but he never angrily confronts his parents and calls them liars. Eventually, the child grows up, and he too becomes a parent who resorts to the same expedient.

"Buddha's paradise is in the distant west, and he is waiting to save us. Let us face west and pray." The evening sky of the sunset is beautiful all over the world. This beauty must have been utilized to remind man of the beauty of paradise. This may be an expedient, but it is not a lie. Because of this teaching, countless people must have received comfort. Just as a child understands when he reaches a certain age that Santa is an expedient, so a man will, when he attains a certain mental maturity, realize that Buddha does not exist in the west, but has always existed within himself.

It is said that Buddha taught some 84,000 teachings, but all were "expedients," tailored to fit the quality of the man. Just as kindergarten has a kindergarten curriculum, so an elementary school has an elementary curriculum. If Buddha taught in a way suited to the qualitative level of certain individuals, then to cling forever to that expedient and not advance beyond it is not good. A parent would be troubled, too, if his twenty-year-old child still waited for Santa.

The danger faced by most religious leaders is that their distinction between what is true and what is expedient is too vague. It would become a problem if a child stuck to his belief in Santa forever, but to try to make him believe in it forever is just as bad. Most religious leaders seem to fall into this pattern. Because a man once learned in theological school that Christ is the one and only son of God and saviour, he asserts, even after turning fifty, that this is true and audaciously claims that Buddha and Lao-tsze are "fake saints." His mental age must be said to be about ten.

All expedient ways are precious. But unless man graduates from them and climbs to a higher level of truth, an expedient may turn into his enemy. The elevator was invented to make ascending to a higher floor easy. If it were to be used as a room and we placed a desk and bed in it, its purpose would be lost. I can't help but think that religious leaders have changed the elevator into a room. "This is an elevator. Please take out the bed and put it into a bedroom." "But this *is* my bedroom." If only religious leaders were involved, it would not matter so much, but they lead believers to commit the same mistake. They may not actually say, "If you go to the church of a different denomination, you will be punished," but they imply it by their attitude, thus preventing the believers from study-ing the good points of other religions. Leaders entrusted to lead believers to a state of godliness imprison them in the lower state of expediency and do not want to free them. Sectarianism not only destroys world peace, but also imprisons its followers. "Hell is where religious leaders go," surely this is a word from God.

*Oneness of all religions.*   I do not mean it is wrong to belong to the religious groups that presently exist. While belonging to a religious group, however, do not allow yourself to be trapped at the level of expedients, but progress straight on to the "truth" within it. All forms of religion are fingers pointing to the moon of "truth." If you look only at the finger, you will never see the moon. As long as you cling to sectarianism, you will never know the "truth." But as long as you have this understanding, you can belong to any religion. All religions are headed toward and point toward the one and only Truth. Consequently all religoins belong to you. By studying the good points of all religions, you are being most faithful to your own.

Though the paths in the foothills may differ,
the moon seen from the summit is the same.

This old poem teaches that any religion will suffice. It implies that we are all looking at the same moon, but from different directions. What I am trying to say here is different. All religions are headed for the one truth, but by itself, each religion is just a part of the truth, a very deficient part of the whole. Therefore, by studying the good points of the other religious groups, we should create a "whole and complete" religion. That is what I am trying to say. When one looks at a tree from the top, it looks like a countless mass of leaves and branches, but when one looks at it from the ground, it is just one trunk, separa-ting into branches. Similarly, there seem to be countless religious groups, but when looked at in reality, there is just one truth divided into many sects. When we understand that the "origin is one," then even though we may belong to a small religious group, the walls of our group can be blown away. One leaf and a neighboring leaf seem like separate existences. But when traced to their origin, they all come from the same root. This is the ground of the feeling that all religions are essentially one—and the reason you can truly respect other religions. Then naturally you can begin to see good points in other religions, and instinctively you will begin to adopt them. Therefore, though religious differences may continue outwardly, their contents will gradually approach the "whole and complete."

"When you go to bed, practice deep breathing ten times, putting power in the *tanden*. Then you will stop going to the bathroom at night." This will help the man, but it is not the true way. It is an expedient. Nevertheless, when a person is not able to practice the real way, a temporary, easier method must be taught.

"Massage your body with a towel wrung out in cold water. Then you will stop catching cold." This is a simple practice taught at a beginner's level of understanding. Actually, the breathing method, correct diet, exercises and mental health are all necessary.

From the standpoint of the true way, each religion is merely a part of what was referred to above as the "oneness of all religions." A part is fine. While practicing it, you will eventually realize you must enter something deeper and broader. Do not mistake the part for the whole.

# The Way of Deliverance

## UNDERSTANDING THE WAY OF DELIVERANCE

*Recognizing the phenomenal world as suffering.* Man's most heartfelt desires culminate, I believe, in "freedom." When one compares liberalism with communism, the impression received is that capitalism is liberal and communism is not. But communism is an ideology that emerged from a deep yearning for "freedom for life," so it too can be considered "liberal."

Man's feeling of unhappiness is, in substance, a feeling of lack of "freeness," so when he grasps this "freedom," he can be satisfied. But in this world of birth and death, everything gives the feeling of something lacking. A youth who declares with feigned anger, "I didn't want to be born, but my parents brought me into this world arbitrarily," then marries, and soon he in turn is having children. No one wants to get old, but gray hairs start to increase. We don't want to get sick, but the blood pressure climbs. We don't want to die, but we know our turn is coming. No one wants to be separated from loved ones, but we must part. There are some poeple we do not want to see at all, but we bump into them. Things we want, we cannot get, and things we don't like, we cannot get rid of. Buddha taught us of the shackles of this phenomenal world by describing it in terms of the aforementioned "eight sufferings."

When man understands that despite all his efforts, he cannot escape from these eight sufferings, he also knows that man can never be truly happy in this world. But he also confirms that the desire for freedom rooted within man's heart cannot be erased. This is the reason for the birth of religious culture.

God is, in short, infinite freedom. That this does not exist as a mere desire but as an actuality, was discovered by religion. "God's world" came to be spoken of in Shinto as "the plain of high heaven," in Buddhism as the "pure land," and in Christianity as "heaven." The degree of sureness about this world differs from religion to religion, but it is all the same in that it was discovered after Herculean effort on man's part.

So in this world where man cannot help but be overwhelmed by a feeling of restriction or unfreeness, when God and God's world are discovered, at that instant man can acquire the "feeling of freedom." This is not the freedom generally thought of in the phenomenal world. The true meaning of "happiness" is a "feeling of happiness" and nothing else. When this "feeling of freedom" enters our hearts, instantly it changes to a "feeling of happiness." This feeling is in itself happiness and, simultaneously, the motivating power "phenomenon of happiness."

Actually, if the world of suffering were the only world man had to live in, he would not be able to survive. Man may lightly say that mankind will be a nihilated if the sun should be lost forever, but as a psychological fact, it is impossible for man to imagine a world completely cut off from the sun's ray. "Well, we have night," some may say, but there is still the conviction that on the morrow, the sun will again rise in the east. That is why he can fantasize nonchalantly about a world without a sun.

The reason man can conceive the idea that this is a world of suffering is that somewhere in his mind the image of a "world without suffering" flashes on. A man can say, "This is ugly" only because he has a "beautiful image" in his mind. Likewise, a man who talks of a "world of suffering" is always one who has seen the existence of a "happy world." That is the escape route which makes it possible for man to continue living despite trials and tribulations. The ancient saints discovered this "escape." This is the world of god presented to mankind today.

If God's world existed only as an idea, however deeprooted, its value would be meagre, just as gold ore would be valueless underground. Only after it is dug out and made into jewelry does its acquire living value. It is the same way with God's world. Only when it becomes man's "word," an expressed thought, can it give a great feeling of freedom and happiness.

In short, man's unhappiness results from his lack of the feeling of freedom. Lack of the feeling of freedom means he has not yet become aware of the reality of the world of freedom. A parent may set up a trust fund for his child, but if the child never learns of it, he will feel poor forever.

During World War II when we were interned in the Minidoka Relocation Center in Idaho, the narrow but deep Snake River flowed outside the barbed wire fences. One day a youth got out through the fence and committed suicide. He left behind a simple note, "When I am reborn, I want to be a Caucasian." It was a poignant note, arousing great sympathy, but if this youth had known of the actuality of God's world, the feeling of freedom would have comforted his heart and may have prevented such a tragic end.

*Paradise of the three dharma seals.*   The question of the true existence of "God's world" is a problem pursued not only by Buddhist and Christian thinkers but also by the philosophers of the world, but they all seem to fall short when it comes to logical proof. I too engaged in the search, reading as many books of great thinkers as possible, but still did not come across a completely satisfying logical proof. In the end, they all come to the conclusion that logically "God's world" is only a product of man's imagination. Fearing that this would not convince man in this computer age, I continued my quest for a logical proof of God for over thirty years. It would seem likely that there have been earlier men who worked out the same logic and reached the same conclusions I did, but I have yet to find them, so if someone among my readers does know of such works, please refer them to me.

The way of deliverance is based on Buddha's "three dharma seals." Traditionally these three dharma seals have been called the ensign of Buddhism. Where they were properly expounded, there Buddhism was, and where they were not, Buddhism was not. Most teachers have held that the ensign was a standard-bearer saying, "Here is Buddhism." Few, if any, have said that it was the very heart of Buddha's enlightenment. In that sense, I believe that Rev. Entai Tomomatsu of the Kanda Temple was a rare leader in the emphasis he placed on the three dharma seals.

I have separated the way of deliverance into four parts: the law of impermanence, the law of nonself, the law of freedom, and the law of equality. Buddha's three dharma seals consist of three items "non-permanence, non-ego and nirvana," but I have chosen to consider nirvana under the two headings of "freedom" and "equality."

The law of impermanence separates into the impermanence of life in longitudinal perspective and moment by moment impermanence. The former means that everything that is born must someday die. The latter means that everything that is born undergoes change every instant, every second.

The law of nonself separates into nonself dependent origination and immutable dependent origination. Nonself dependent origination means that all things, including human beings, have absolutely no free will and change only according to environment and circumstance. Immutable dependent origination means that everything changes according to given conditions and that there are absolutely no exceptions.

The law of freedom means that the true aspect of life is "infinite freedom."

The law of equality means that you are not the only one with "infinite freedom," for everyone and everything possesses "infinite freedom."

Accordingly, the law of impermanence and the law of nonself concern the "phenomenal world," whereas freedom and equality are concerned with the true features of the "real world." Impermanence and nonself constitute one pair of yin-yang principles, and freedom and equality another. Again, impermanence-nonself and freedom-equality also form a pair of ying-yang principles. These three pairs conform to what I call the "principle of the four limbs," namely, the left arm and right arm, the left leg and right leg, and the two arms and two legs.

LAW OF IMPERMANENCE

*Impermanence of any one life.* Anything that has come into existence will cease to exist. This truth has been summarized in the formula, "All created things are impermanent." The word "things" here means all created things in the universe, so even the earth, too, must someday perish. How much more so for things and beings that appear on the earth. The sun and stars too must one day perish like all things in this universe. Nothing is permanent. Like the truth that $2+2=4$, this is a truth no one can deny. When this truth is rightly understood, man will make a 180-degree aboutface. If he does not change, this only proves that he does not understand the "law of impermanence."

At the moment a death sentence is pronounced, there is not a single man who does not undergo a change. This is what was meant by a 180-degree aboutface. Ask a centenarian if a hundred years does not seem like a long time. He will doubtless reply, "No, in one way it seems long, but again many experiences seem to have happened only yesterday." The feeling of time is a very subjective thing. On nights when you sleep soundly, you feel on awaking that you have just gone to sleep. But on sleepless, restless nights, the time seems to drag by so slowly that you feel you are aging. Buddha perceived the relativity of time. He knew that a hundred years was but an empty dream, that while desperately trying to evade death, man had to die. What a pitiful being am I! And how pitiful are all men! Every one of us has been sentenced to death. The instant Buddha became aware of the impermanence of all things, he became a changed person. This is the key to attaining a disposition to diligence, a loving nature, a sense of sinlessness, and a sense of freedom.

When a man is truly awakened to impermanence, he becomes a man who puts forth effort. How precious each day is! We truly relish the joy of each living moment. And this naturally brings forth a spirit of diligence.

When man truly comprehends impermanence, he becomes a man characterized by love. He cannot help but sympathize with his fellow men who are soon to be killed. All feelings of hate or rancor are washed away.

When impermanence is truly perceived, the conviction of man's sinlessness is attained. It was a mistake to think we had to die. Things that are born and disappear are not real existences. An actually existing thing should never perish. What disappears and perishes never had real existence. No one believes that the image in a mirror is an actual existence, because it appears and disappears. "Things that appear and disappear" were "nonexistent" from the beginning. To think otherwise would be like a monkey thinking that his reflection in the mirror represented the presence of another monkey. It is a mistake to think "I was born." Since appearing and disappearing things are originally nonexistent, I was never born. Therefore, I cannot die. Of course, in this phenomenal world, birth and death are reflected. But this involves not my true self, but only "myself as reflected in a mirror." My figure may disappear from the mirror, but this does not mean I have disappeared. My true self has never embraced the sin we call "death." Then it is that the mind that had been trembling in the face of death suddenly brightens. This we call the sinlessness of man.

When man awakens to impermanence, he attains the conviction of man's freedom. Though the phenomenal world is reflected, it does not exist. A dream exists while we are dreaming, but once we awaken and realize it was a dream, it no longer exists as a reality. The instant we perceive the phenomenal world for what it is, it absolutely ceases to exist. When one understands this, his true self appears in all its brilliance. It is a self that possesses infinite freedom. Just as the other side of the mountain cannot be seen unless we climb to its summit, one's true self cannot be seen unless one truly understands that the "phenomenal world is essentially nonexistent." A dog's true nature is hidden as long as he is tied to a leash. The instant he is unchained, he will start frisking about. This is the dog's true nature. The true self, a self possessing infinite freedom, can be understood the instant one perceives the truth of the nonexistence of the phenomenal world. Buddha called this "Nirvana," and in Mahayana Buddhism it is called "nothingness."

It should be understood, however, that "nothingness" involves two kinds of knowing. One is to know "the nonreality of phenomena," the other to know one's "true self." The word "Nirvana" quite literally contains both of these meanings, as does the word "Nothingness." But the explanations of earlier thinkers have proved insufficient. "The nonreality of phenomena" is an established theory, but nobody seems to have defined "nothingness" as free self.

Thus the first two points in this explanation of impermanence have concerned effort and love in the phenomenal world, and the last two have concerned sinlessness and freedom in the real world.

*Impermanence of each moment.* That all things born must perish is a truth that concerns either the past or the future. But moment by moment impermanence is concerned with the "now." That all things change constantly is axiomatic for present-day physics. But how is it that things change every moment?

To state the conclusion at the outset, things change because they never really existed. When a cup is pushed, it moves. Why does it move? If it were a thing that had real existence, it could not change its position. How can the picture on a movie screen move? It moves because it does not really exist, because it is only a momentary appearance. That is why different pictures can be projected one after the other. If the reflected picture had true existence, it would have to be taken off and removed, but there is no such need. Since it never existed from the beginning, there is no need to remove it. It disappears by itself. The reason all things in the phenomenal world change is that they, like the motion picture, are constantly appearing and disappearing. A motion picture changes images about twenty times a second, but the rate of conversion of the phenomenal world is like that of an electron of mathematical swiftness. In the sutras, there are metaphors of the flow of the river and the shape of flames. When we watch a burning candle, it seems to have a single flame, but actually at each and every moment, one flame dies out and a new one flares up. The sutras teach that the phenomenal world is precisely the same.

All things flow away like water in a river, transmigrating by itself, moving without being pushed, changing constantly like fire. When this aspect is seen for what it is, man's outlook on life changes completely. Prior to this recognition, all things in the universe seemed to have firm existence, to be immovable, unchangeable, and even to assert their right to exist. But the instant man learns the truth of moment by moment impermanence, he finds that all things in nature have only a frail existence, are eailsy movable, are as changeable as marbles rolling down a hill. With this recognition surges forth a life-creating hope. Courage to purify the phenomenal world increases, the will to rebuild the environment becomes stronger, and the conviction is attained that life is a great and joyous art.

*Discovery of the truth of nonself.* "The truth of nonself" is an abbreviation of the formula, "All creating things have no self." This formula stands in a yin-yang relationship with the first dharma seal, "All created things are impermanent." The truth of impermanence regarded all phenomena from the aspect of the flow of time, but nonself is a truth that regards phenomena from the aspect of their interconnectedness in *space*. "All creating things" contrasts with "all created things" and means "all things in a position to create."

Then who or what are the things in a position to produce or create? Everything is. Even a desk creates the power to carry things. A vase creates the power to hold water so it will not leak. A flower creates beauty within man's heart. All things have an effect on or affect others, and this interconnectedness is referred to as a "law." There is not one thing or person that does not affect others. But among them all, man is thought to be the greatest "influencer," so for the time being, it will be convenient to regard man as the subject of this law.

"Nonself" means "there is no self." But what, then, is the "self"? It means a "possessor of free will." Free will means to have the power to act on one's own accord. It signifies a central existence having the power to decide freely whether it will start or stop, sit or stand, avoid evil, do good, etc. "I did." "You did." "I did not do it." "You did not do it." As can be judged from these expressions, it is generally taken as common sense that everyone possesses free will. Both before and after Buddha, everyone born as a human being has without exception thought, "There is a self." Only one man discerned the truth, "Man has absolutely no free will. He only conducts himself in accordance with the conditions supplied to him." This man was Buddha, who after six years of ascetic practices, made this discovery as he sat under the bodhi tree.

The "law of nonself" is the truth whose discovery makes Buddhism what it is. When Buddhism is contrasted with other religions, this "law of nonself" appears as unique. Consequently, anyone wishing to understand Buddhism must first of all endeavor to grasp this "law of nonself."

*Depiction of the subjugation of the demons.* The most important doctrine in Christianity is the doctrine of original sin. In Buddhism, the most important teaching is that of "ignorance." Sadly, a man is given a "name" when he is born. This is the chief instigation for creating delusion. From the moment we are born, we are called by our "name." It is only natural that deep in our consciousness, we should believe, "I exist." When we go to school, the teacher calls us by name. At work, the name still follows us, and for taxes and licenses, we continuously use and are called by the name until we die. It is no wonder man is convinced that "I exist."

But truth is truth. Three plus three equals six. "That is inconvenient, let's make it five," we might say, but six can be only six. "Man has no free will. He does not have the power to decide between good and bad." On first hearing this, some people get angry. "Such nonsense! Look at me. I have free will. To this day, I have thought things out,

made up my own mind, and acted accordingly. How dare anyone call this a delusion."
Others, while not becoming angry, feel confused and perplexed by the teaching of nonself.
The picture entitled "Subjugating the demons and attaining enlightenment" teaches the
tenacity of original sin and ignorance.

*Principle of conditionedness*.   All human behavior, including not only acts but thoughts
as well, are determined by previous "conditions." The cash register counts as the keys are
punched and at the end shows the total. It seems to be counting precisely, but the cash
register itself is not doing the calculating. It cannot help counting because its keys are
being punched. Man is similar to this cash register. It seems that he is thinking about all
kinds of things in minute detail, but actually he is nothing but a machine punched into
action by the keys of circumstance.

   The phrase "I have decided" means only that one is acting in accordance with the sum
total of keypunched calculations from an infinite past. It is not that "I have decided" in
such-and-such a way. The decision is an inevitable consequence of previous conditions.

   Many find this truth worrying. "If that were so, man would lose all hope. Then what
would you say? If circumstances were everything, it would be useless to talk of good or
bad. Human society itself would go to pieces."

   The fact is that for someone whose blood has become impure through wrong diet, and
whose breathing is uneven from not practicing meditation, to try to comprehend this truth
that Buddha found only after exerting himself to the utmost, is decidedly impossible.
On the other hand, unless some kind of relationship is established, this truth will forever
remain hidden from such people. Therefore I will try to explain it.

   "Demonstrate to me, in any area whatever, that you have free will."

   "I am now drinking tea, but not because circumstances force me to do so. Of my own
free will, I stretched out my arm and brought the cup to my lips. As proof, I am also able
to decide not to drink it."

   "That's precisely the point. You are now going through all those motions and demon-
strating to me because we had just discussed 'nonself.' If the subject had not been brought
up, you would not have put on a demonstration. Likewise, you were able to drink the tea
because it was served to you, and because you came here on business, we were able to
have this conversation. If you had not come, the tea would not have been served, and if you
had not had any business, you would not have visited me. All man's actions involve anteced-
ent conditions. Impelled by them, he has to act. A flying bullet does not think, 'I am
flying.' A moving car does not think, 'I am running.' Man is absolutely the same. The
only difference is that he believes, 'I have free will.' "

   "If man has no free will, then aren't court trials nonsense?"

   "No, they aren't. A man is not punished because he has done wrong. A man is dis-
ciplined in the desire to provide a condition that will make him better. Likewise, with
regard to others, an 'example' is shown, as a condition that will teach them not to commit
crimes. In the world of human beings, there are no 'good' or 'bad' men. Only the distinction between good and bad behavior exists. Good behavior is a good thing, so we

should practice it. Bad behavior is bad, so we should avoid it. That's all there is to it."

"This 'doing' or 'not doing,' isn't it 'free will'?"

"No, it is not. It is a way of encouraging, and as such a new 'condition,' so that man will have a chance to improve."

"This 'trying to improve,' is it not free will?"

"No. Man, in his desire for happiness, is only saying 'I must do good.' A 'desire for happiness' is not free will. From the moment he is born a man, the desire is there, like an infant's instinctively grasping for his mother's breasts."

As the conversation progresses, the truth seems to become a little clearer. The majority of people seem to grasp a little of the truth of "nonself" after such a conversation. I call the truth of nonself the "truth of lamentation." Man has hope only when he has free will, and when confronted with the fact that there is no free will, he turns pale in shock. "Slave of conditions," what a tragic fact! Yesterday, head of a nation; today, a prisoner exposed to public scorn. This fate is not limited to Mussolini and Tojo alone. A law exists which makes this fate possible for anyone.

*Value of the truth of no self in nonself.*   This is the point at which there suddenly arises the disposition to "diligence." This diligence is not just ordinary effort. It is the unconsciously superhuman effort a man makes when trying to escape from a fire-engulfed home, that drives him to search frantically for a place of safety, that makes him try to escape even when told not to, or run even when told to stand still. This striving first appears in the form of seeking the truth, when man is forced to make a 180-degree turn in his way of life.

Next, a "loving nature" will be born. I am a pitiful slave of conditions and he too is a sad slave of conditions. How, then, can we hate one another? Perhaps he acted rude to me, but there was undoubtedly a condition that made him unable to do otherwise. One understands from the bottom of his heart what a fragile thing it is to be a "child of man." And from that realization there rushes forth an inexhaustible feeling of sympathy and love.

Next is the "sense of sinlessness." They say man is good or bad. But this is only said out of delusion. Just as a car is not at fault when it falls into a ditch, a man is not to be blamed even when he commits a crime. It is only that his "conditions" were bad. There may be some people living with the gnawing thought, "What I did at that time was wrong," but this is a misconception. Man does not possess the least power to commit wrong. "Man is sinless!" With this realization, a cry of rejoicing can be heard welling up from the bottom of one's heart.

Then comes the "sense of freedom." When man understands that he himself does not exist, he can confirm "Nirvana-nothingness." He discovers his true self, as free and unhindered as the wide blue sky. He grasps a self that possesses an absolute free will. The "false self" is replaced by a forever indestructible real self. This is the self we call "God."

*Truth of no obscurity in nonself.*   The foregoing has been a brief explanation of the truth of no self in nonself. This truth contrasts with that of impermanence, whose virtues consist of exactly the same four items, "diligence," "love," "sinlessness" and "freedom."

Only when the law of impermanence and the law of nonself form a yin-yang connection will the multiplication principle be able to function, thus bringing to completion the four virtues of diligence, love, sinlessness and freedom.

We turn now to the study of the truth of no obscurity in nonself. This expression means "the non-deceptive truth of nonself." All things are always determined by "conditions." Just as water assumes a round shape when poured into a round container, or a square shape when poured into a square one, nothing remains unchanged when touched by "conditions." When a steering wheel is turned to the left, the wheels turn left, and when it is turned to the right, they turn right. The truth of the unobscurable nonself is obvious and never deceives. This idea is similar to that of "law" as used in science, but this law is a continuation of the truth of no self in nonself and a confirmation of the pliability one attains after attainment of freedom, as a result of which there springs up a strong feeling of hope. A picture is drawn according to the way paint and brush are used, so an artist concentrates on mastering them. But if the artist has no artistic talent, the best paint and brush in the world are of no value. In the same way, if a scientist knew the unobscurable nonself but did not possess freedom, his knowledge would be worthless.

Man always changes according to conditions. If he encounters good he becomes good, and if he comes in touch with bad he becomes bad. This pliability functions to elevate and increase the volition to create human life. Therefore, the truth of the unobscurable nonself is, in contrast to moment by moment impermanence, the giver of hope in the highest degree. Reduced to a concise formula, this is summarized in the expression "The world that changes, instant by instant, according to form." "Instant by instant" refers to moment by moment impermanence. "According to form" refers to the unobscurable nonself. (Space limitations prevent fuller explanation here. Readers are referred to my *Bannin no Bukkyō* [Buddhism for all people]).

## LAW OF FREEDOM

*Deity in Buddhism and other religions.*

> A flower blooming fragrantly today is gone tomorrow,
> Nothing has durability in our world.
> Pass over the ever-changing mountain today,
> Never be attached to shallow dreams, nor intoxicated.

This ode is said to have been written by St. Kōbō. It expresses well the important truth, "All visible things are impermanent." Only when one understands impermanence will the desire arise to seek out and find the real, the permanent world.

> There is no rain
> That falls sideways of itself.
> 'Tis only the wind that beats
> Against the window at midnight.

This verse was composed by St. Rissho. It teaches the important truth, "All phenomenal things have no self." When one understands that he is "selfless," that he is "a slave of condition," a desire arises within him to seek and find the Infinite Self.

Without a "seeking mind," there is no day of discovery. The original inhabitants of

Los Angeles had no means of discovering the rich supply of oil underground. They did not have a seeking mind. The truths of impermanence and nonself become one with the truth of yin-yang and give birth to a "truth-seeking mind" in man. From ancient times, the truth of dependent origination has always meant this truth of oneness. Another way of putting it is that the degree of truth-seeking mind one possesses is in direct proportion to the degree of his understanding of the truth of dependent origination. Those who personally experience the horrors of war are more earnest in their pursuance of world peace. A drunkard is not aware of the dangers of crossing an intersection. An alert person is aware of the dangers and crosses only when it is safe.

When a man seeks the truth in this manner, he discovers that beneath his feet there is an eternal and infinitely free world. Man abhors "death" only because there is "eternal life" existing somewhere. Man hates "restriction" because there is "free life" somewhere. A dance teacher keeps correcting and scolding her pupil's dancing because, in the teacher's mind, there exists a "world of perfect beauty." In all things "ugliness" is recognizable only because "beauty of the mind" exists. Man can recognize death and restriction as bad only because "eternity and freeness" actually exist in his mind. And this actual existence is, indeed, an "infinite reality."

"How much do you want eternal free life?"

"I want it unlimitedly."

This is a natural answer. This unlimited desire, which mankind as a whole possesses, is proof that an unlimited eternal free life actually exists. The reply "This much is sufficient" implies "there is a limit" and thus that the object in question cannot be said to actually exist, because anything that is limited must one day inevitably perish. Only the unlimited has reality.

From whatever angle you look at it, the phenomenal world is not a reality. A thing that is not a reality does not "really exist." That it does not "really exist" means that it "never really existed." Figures that are reflected on a movie screen do not "really exist," so they are "in themselves nonexistent." The phenomenal world is truly in itself nonexistent. This is the reason the law of Nirvana-nothingness was established.

The phenomenal world is, in itself, nothingness. In contrast, the "unlimited, eternal, free life" is, in itself, a reality. Here "God" manifests his whole countenance. "God," as spoken of in most religions, is the "God" reflected in the mind, and big or small, perfect or imperfect, the form that is manifested takes shape in a way that mirrors the receivers' state of mind. The uniqueness of the god of Buddhism lies in the absolute nonexistence of phenomenon, in the absolute nonexistence of sin and evil, yet nonetheless a subsequent manifestation of "unlimited, free and eternal life." For a picture drawn on a blackboard to be perfect, two conditions must coincide. First, the blackboard must be wiped clean, and second, the picture must be drawn well. The weakness of religions in general is that they have not gone through the procedure of erasing the blackboard clean.

"God created this world"

"Then why does created man commit sin?"

"That is because, because . . ." and as an exersice in logic, a conversation of this kind soon comes to an end. Because of this dormant weakness, it is difficult to attain strong belief.

As for their cognition of the "unlimitedly eternal free life," people are limited by categories derived from the finite, leading them to speak of a god of the sun, a god of the wind, a god of thunder, etc. This is poles apart from the "unlimited" as meant in Buddhism. To seriously assert, for instance, that mankind has only one savior is proof that men holding that view look on God as finite. The Buddhist standpoint is that God is truly infinitely free and therefore provides an infinite numberr of saviors.

The God of Buddhism expresses both the cleanly-wiped blackboard and the well-drawn picture, so no other greater God can be found. Buddha called this "Nirvana." The discovery of this Nirvana is the content of the enlightenment he attained under the bodhi tree, bringing forth the enlightenment that led him to recognize himself as the "father of mankind."

*Life as a shackle*.   "Hey, let's go out and have a drink after work tonight." On their way home from the office, two fellow workers drink away their frustrations and arrive home late, full of trepidation. This is a double loss. Many repeat this over and over again. Drinking liquor and getting intoxicated is one form of deliverance. The more he drinks, the more he becomes a conqueror of the realm and for some hours he is "delivered," but what awaits him is bad. What is the true objective of drinking? It is nothing else than the "feeling of freedom." It is only natural, in fact inevitable, that a man broken down by a "feeling of restraint" should instinctively reach out for a "feeling of freedom." Even a woman, when she feels irritated by a "feeling of restriction," will go out and buy a hat or dress, or if she doesn't have the money, will go window shopping and return home comforted with some degree of "freedom."

As a man, one cannot be happy if he is "shackled," yet no man can live without "shackles." By seeking a solution to this contradiction through liquor and vanity, man's life is only made more difficult. This is why man needs "the world of religion."

"I am in and of myself an eternally free God." When a man understands this, an unlimited "sense of freedom" rushes forth, and liquor and vanity become unnecessary. The more difficult life is, the more we must master "deliverance." With God, there is not a single problem that cannot be solved, for God is "unlimited freedom."

## LAW OF EQUALITY

*Dangers of an illogical doctrine of equality*.   When a man understands that he is a god, it might seem that all his problems are solved, but there is another, contrasting truth that needs to be considered. That is the "law of equality." Buddha's compassion, Confucius' humanism and Jesus' love were expressions of this law of equality. Even in governments, there is not a political slogan that does not praise equality. From birth, man desires and seeks "equality" as well as "freedom." "Freedom and love" are the whole countenance of man's desire. Nothing else is worthy to be called desire. Man's craving for fame and fortune, love and health, and all other wishes are, in the long run, merely cravings whereby to satisfy the two instinctive desires for "freedom and love." Therefore, when man is overcome with a "feeling of unhappiness," this is nothing other than a lack of "freedom and love." This is the reason all the saints that have ever appeared, without exception, emphasized love or equality.

What is "equality"? First, an affirmation of the identity of one's self and others is necessary. The great value of the truth of no self in nonself is manifested here. Suppose it were possible for man to have free will. The question, why do some men incline toward the good and others toward evil, would then make it possible to infer the existence of good free will and bad free will. The conclusion to be drawn would then be that men are by nature not equal. If we start out from such an uncertain conception, no matter how much we chante "equality," in our minds we will be thinking, "Men are made unequal." The mouth and mind would be divided. This is the reason the "doctrine of equality" as usually conceived does not have the firm support of the general public.

"Our race is a God-chosen people, with a mission to unite the whole world." There are at least four groups of people who make this statement. They have fallen into this superstitious belief because of blind adherence to the teaching, "Man has free will." Made drunk by some slight superiority of past history, they willfully decide that the future will be the same. All this derives from the thought, "I" exist. For a politician to think thus can be left undiscussed, but for a religious leader to do so is a problem.

"In his great, divine providence, God first led the white people into his fold, then the Asians, and finally the blacks, and He is continuing His missionary work." This might seem a likely thing for a Caucasian minister to say, but actually it was a Japanese minister I heard preaching this with a serious look. It is proof there is no backbone in the "doctrine of equality" he preaches. This can happen when one becomes a captive of the free-will theory.

Man has by nature no free will. According to the principle of conditionedness, man only appears and disappears. When this is comprehended, the true equality of man is understood. A so-called good man is good only because what conditioned him was good; a bad man is bad only because what conditioned him was bad. There is no essential difference whatever. Even though past history may have been in one's favor, there is no guarantee that the future will be similarly propitious. Whether it be a race or an individual, when the conditions become bad, decline is inevitable. Therefore, one should deeply impress on one's mind the "law of dependent origination" and strive with diligence. This is the wisdom of the wise.

*Sadaparibhuta Bodhisattva.*   Buddha's teaching about equality, since it is based on an understanding of the law of the universe, is in a completely different category from that of an opportunistic "doctrine of equality." Buddha, in becoming aware of the truth "I am a god," was at the same time enlightened to the truth "Everything is god," thus attaining the greatest love in the universe.

"I rob others, but so do you. All men are equal." The run-of-the-mill "doctrine of equality" is a means of justifying one's wrongdoings. Many lawyers and labor union leaders seem to fall into this category. Therefore, the people who need to be vindicated and laborers who need to be protected seem never to achieve happiness.

Buddha's doctrine of equality does not mean that men are equal in possessing a thievish nature, but that they are equal in "godliness." When a man becomes aware of his own "godliness," he sees the "godliness" in others; when he sees the "godliness" in others, he can see his own "godliness." He who thinks of himself as a thief will always suspect others of being thieves. Man can evaluate others only as highly as he evaluates himself One who thinks of another as a thief may someday become a thief himself. This is the law of the unobscurable nonself. Everyone is influenced by and comes to resemble whatever he touches.

"Now, straighten your posture . . ." If the Yoga teacher thus instructing his pupil also has a warm prayer within him, "May his posture become straight," then the teacher's posture will have become straight before the pupil's.

If the teacher says "Stand up straight" while thinking "What a crooked back," not only will the pupils posture not become straight, but the teacher's posture will also slump. To truly respect another is none other than to truly respect one's self. Endeavouring to see the good in others is ultimately only a way of elevating one's own self.

The lotus was used as a simile very often by the Buddha when preaching. The lotus bears many meanings, and to explain them in detail would take us down many bypaths, but in the main the lotus is a symbol of equality. Even in a dirty swamp, the lotus blooms purely. No matter how ugly a man may look outwardly, he too has a pure Buddha nature. Do not be fooled by outward appearances and look down on others with contempt. This is the simile of the lotus. Many sutras have the word "lotus" in their title. This is due to Buddha's enlightenment regarding equality.

This does not mean that only our fellow men are "equals." Dogs and cats, cows and horses, worms and snails, pines and oaks and nameless grasses growing in the fields —they all, impartially, possess Buddha nature! This was the enlightenment of Buddha. Sadaparibhuta Bodhisattva, who deeply respected and praised everyone without any discrimination, is mentioned prominently in the Lotus Sutra. It is recorded that this Bodhisattva was a Buddha in a previous existence.


# The Mind-Only Way

## UNDERSTANDING THE MIND-ONLY WAY

*The wonder of Buddhist psychology.*   Man's happiness is directly proportionate to the strength of his belief in what traditional Buddhist terminology means by "freedom and equality" and what in modern language is referred to as "freedom and love." Yet mere understanding and assent to this truth does not mean that one will instantly become happy. This is because "understanding" and "mind" occupy different spheres. Modern psychologists separate these two into "surface consciousness" and "subconsciousness," but they do not begin to come near the psychology preached by Buddha. Just as modern doctors have finally begun to understand the value of Yoga as a health way, modern psychologists have just begun to be amazed at the thoroughness of Buddhist psychology. An outstanding psychologist was quoted in *Life* magazine as saying "Buddhist psychology should be researched first before entering into the study of modern psychology." All Buddhists know the term "five aggregates"; if a psychologist truly understood them, he would be an amazing psychologist.

The "material aggregate" means the "world allotted to us" at birth.

The "perception aggregate" refers to that dimension wherein we perceive this world with eyes, ears, nose, tongue, body, and mind.

The "conception aggregate" is that dimension where we decide how to interpret and render the "perceived world" and store it in the mind.

The "action aggregate" is the dimension of behavior. It rests on the inevitable reflex action that arises in relation to the "conceived world" stored within us.

The "subconscious aggregate" means that the actions of our body, words, and mind will be recorded without fail in our subconsciousness and never disappear. And this deep, many-layered subconsciousness, in accordance with its contents, will change the "allotted world."

This is only a brief explanation of the five aggregates. To explain them in detail, and to enable modern people to understand them correctly, would require a huge book.

The "mind" is infinitely deep. The ocean is said to be infinitely deep, too, but it has a bottom. The sky is said to be infinitely high, but the atmosphere is quite a thin layer. But the infinitude of the "mind" does not have limits like these. The consciousness is deep and many-layered, but there must be a limit somewhere—this is the standpoint of most modern psychologists. The popular impression is that psychologists have their patients lie down on a sofa and start talking of whatever comes into their minds. This is not meaningless, but my desire for them as professionals is that they delve deeper into their study of psychology. If one wanted to study and the materials were not available, there would be little he could do about it, but in this case the materials already exist—a Buddhist psychology which is very thoroughgoing.

Why was Buddhist psychology able to delve so deeply? It is because Buddhists grasped the principle of conditionedness. That man is what his conditions make him is a great truth in itself, but the truth of conditionedness inevitably leads one to think of "the conditions of a condition."

*Infinite dependent origination.* "When the wind blows, the cooper rejoices." This is the opening line of an old tale told by Buddhist preachers in Japan. When the wind blows, it raises dust. When the dust rises, blindness increases. When blindness increases, demand for the samisen (a three-stringed guitar-like instrument used by the blind for a living) increases. When the need for samisen (made from cat hide) increases, the cat population decreases. When cats become scarce, rats increase. When rats increase, they gnaw on tubs. When tubs are gnawed, the cooper rejoices. This may be difficult for the younger generation to understand, but older people will understand it readily. The preachers used this parable to teach the "principle of conditionedness" or, in an older phrase, "dependent origination." This parable ends with the cooper rejoicing, but actually the cooper's joy will extend infinitely and spread throughout the world. This is the meaning of the Buddhist term "infinite dependent origination." For one thing to exist, every component in the world has to have interconnections with all the other components. This not only spreads out infinitely in space but in time as well, going back to the infinite past. Again, the existence of a thing means that it will have unlimited influence extending into an infinite future. This is the "principle of conditionedness."

There exists here a thing called "mind." When we consider it through the eyeglasses of the principle of conditionedness, we know that this mind has been affected by each and everything from the beginning of the universe and even from the remotest area of the universe. Accordingly, the treatment for the mind was quite different from that of present-day psychologists. Politicians and scholars frequently use the phrase, "The cause is . . .," but when Buddhist insight is brought into play, the idea of causation becomes much more profound. Listening to or reading news editorials, I have often thought, "What superficial thinking. The public is to be pitied." During the Pacific War, for example, many politicians said the cause was imperialistic aggression, but this was a result of something else. What we have to consider is why such aggression came about.

*Wisdom of practice.* Thus it was that Buddhism studied the mind in accordance with the principle of conditionedness, developed a clear and penetrating psychology, and established a great domain called "the study of consciousness-only." What this resulted in was a thoroughgoing method of introspective evaluation or self-reflection. Emphasis was laid not only on "understanding" but also on its counterpart, "practices for self-improvement." In consequence, the way of practice developed in all directions. How can it be that within one and the same Buddhism contradictory methods of practice are advocated? Some say we should seek enlightenment not in our own strength but in the strength of an Other, while other voices declare that we should do so not in the strength of an Other but in our own strength. Some say we should rely not on a mantra but on meditation, while others insist that the right way is not that of meditation but of the mantra. Some defend the centrality of the precepts and rules, others assign the chief role to meditation and intelligence. There is hardly any limit to the examples that could be given. That there should be such great contradictions within Buddhism makes Christian scholars cock their heads. Dr. Daisetz Suzuki explained in his fluent English the "identity of self-power and other-power," but it is doubtful that his students at Columbia University were able to grasp his meaning.

The reason such great contradictions arose in one and the same Buddhism is that the disciples were very thorough in their psychological self-reflection. All sorts of methods were discovered whereby to reconstruct the "deep, many-layered consciousness." In a way, man has a very pitiful existence. Because of this "deep, many-layered consciousness," he was born with an unlimited burden of karma. A relative may have been an alcoholic who repeatedly tried to stop drinking but could not, and consequently died young. Many say they tried hard to avoid a divorce for the sake of the children, but failed. This shows how fragile man's efforts are.

Freedom and love, when fully understood, hold real power to solve all life's problems.

But even that is relentlessly blown away by the principle of conditionedness that obtains in this phenomenal world. This is the reason for a new development, the "wisdom of practice." The point of this new development is to enable us to hold on to that freedom and love we once grasped. In other words, how can we let this freedom and love sink into our deep, many-layered consciousness?

The answer proposed here has four parts: the way of ideation only, the way of sub-consciousness only, the way of virtue, and the way of faith. The way of ideation only is to know the truth that happiness or unhappiness exists solely in inner feelings. The way of subconsciousness only is to know that happiness or unhappiness can be created only through one's self. The way of virtue is to discern the truth that "I have been a practi-tioner of freedom and love from the immutable past." The way of faith is to see the real existence of a superior virtuous Being who far surpasses my own virtuous self.

"Ideation only" and "subconsciousness only" come under the traditional "mind-only theory." "Virtue" and "faith" conform to the traditional "theory of Buddhahood." "Ideation only" and "subconsciousness only" constitute one yin-yang pair, and "virtue" and "faith" another. The relationship between the first pair and the second is also a yin-yang relation. Together, these sets form, in accordance with the principle of the four limbs, the comprehensive mind-only way.

## WAY OF IDEATION ONLY

*Dimension of the perception aggregate.* However hard man may struggle, he cannot perceive the outer world directly. The only possible way for man to see the outer world is, without exception, through his sensory organs: his eyes, ears, nose, tongue, body, and mind.

One can say that the moon is beautiful, but it is the "moon in the mind" that is beautiful, and to a blind man, the bright moon does not exist. A piano tuner comes to adjust the piano keys. He hits the same key many times, apparently to correct its tone, but as for me, I cannot tell the difference. Man's ears can only detect sound waves between 30,000 and 16 decibels. If he cannot hear sounds outside this range, he is, from the standpoint of a dog or cat, partially deaf. Telescopes and microscopes have been developed to the point where we think the most distant and smallest objects have already been studied, but the truth is we do not yet know even 1/1,000,000th of the universe.

The outer world man senses is, in short, not the outer world itself but only whatever is reflected by his sensory organs. Consequently, the reflection can always differ according to the person. "I have some mushrooms I would like to share with you. Can I bring them over now?" "Thank you for the thought, but I have chronic sinusitis and cannot smell anything. It would be a waste to eat mushrooms without savoring their aroma, so please share them with someone who can really appreciate them." This was the answer I heard over the phone. I found myself unconsciously stroking my nose in appreciation of my sense of smell. If it were only a matter of the connection between nose and mush-rooms, the problem would not amount to much, but in cases where feelings toward words are involved, the problem of sense can become one with momentous results. I was told that in the Pacific War a Japanese communication replying to the Potsdam Proclamation contained the phrase "keep silent." But when received in America, this phrase was translated "ignore," which gave it a much stronger meaning than it had in the original. Because of that one word, it is said that President Truman decided to drop the atomic bomb. Because of an inadequacy in the "sense of what was intended," 200,000 people fell victims. A friend's son was interested in electronics, but did not qualify for the course when the college found out he was color-blind. This is a handicap because being able to distinguish the different colors of the wires is so important in electronics. There are many cases where man's fate is determined by the fitness or unfitness of his senses. This is what is indicated by the Buddhist term "perception aggregate."

*Dimension of the conception aggregate.*   When something is reflected in a particular person's mind by the sensory organs, a response unique to that person is reached in regard to that reflection. For example, suppose there are three persons with about the same degree of ability to smell mushrooms. The instant they see the mushrooms, one may think, "Delicious mushroom," another, "Expensive mushroom," and still another, "Autumn mushroom." The impression always differs from person to person. Therefore, even as they look at the same mushroom, a "mind translation" takes place that is completely separate from sense-perception.

> When you clap your hands, a serving girl appears, fish gather,
> And birds fly away, at the Pond of Sarusawa.

When you clap your hands at the tourist attraction named Sarusawa Pond, a waitress will think she is being summoned, fish will think they are going to be fed, and birds think a gun is being fired.

There is only one sound, but its interpretations differ depending on the hearer. This difference brings about important results in man's life, for this "impression" is the deciding factor in man's happiness or unhappiness. War and peace supposedly make no difference in the flavor of the sweet potato, but many people who looked on it with gratitude during the food-scarce wartime now look down on it disdainfully. People are always happy when they have gratitude within them, and are always unhappy when they feel disdainful. There are many examples of a foolish mother-in-law despising her daughter-in-law and vice versa, but in both cases they are simply making themselves unhappy. Even if there should be a truly bad trait in one of them, the other, merely by thinking "She must have grown up in the midst of bad conditions; how pitiful!" will find a compassionate feeling arising from within. When you understand the truth, "I am a buddha, and all others are buddhas; to despise another is to despise myself," your face will become gentle, and the other party is sure to notice it. Without paying tuition, we are being taught the road to life's happiness. Without undergoing such trials, we cannot even correctly educate our children. For fifteen or twenty years after World War II, the chief demand of Japanese brides was that there be no mother-in-law under the same roof. What stupidity! Were they not aware that before they knew it, they would be in the same position? And something was wrong with the grooms, too. They should have declared, "I will not marry any girl who will not be good to my parents." Only when a woman can qualify for this, can she become a good and loving wife.

Man's happiness or unhappiness is definitely not caused by the outer world. It can only be due to the ideas within our own minds. When this truth is understood, then we may be able to comprehend the vaue of the truth, "Revere the buddha nature of all things." But whether one can willingly think so depends on the person, because this is determined by the conditions that inhere in the deep, many-layered consciousness.

The surface-consciousness is like a seed and the deep, many-layered consciousness like the soil. Even when good seeds are planted, if the soil is bad, the seeds will not grow well. Though you pour in bright thoughts, if the subconsciousness is dark and murky, you cannot brighten it. Both seed and soil are important. Thus along with the knowledge that the distinction between happiness and unhappiness exists only in the mind, the knowledge that one must purify the deep, many-layered consciousness is also important. This is what Buddha taught as the "conception aggregate."

## WAY OF SUBCONSCIOUSNESS ONLY

*Children's education.*  As long as we remember to interpret everything with good faith, there are no problems involving human relations that cannot be solved. As long as we do not forget the principle of conditionedness, we can be truly sympathetic with anyone. There is good or bad in circumstances, but there is absolutely no good or bad in man. True, we do think, "Because he was bad, this happened." But this is the beginning of a mistake. When teaching a child, if you start out with the words, "You are wrong, so . . .," you cannot reason with him. You must first place complete trust in the child as a person, and then say, "This was wrong, let us correct it." Then he will understand. All men want to be respected by their fellow men. It does not come from a base desire such as vanity, but from the intuitive knowledge of man's essential preciousness.

We should understand that there is a great difference between thinking "bad man" and thinking "bad thing." When you think of another as a bad person, then even more quickly than the other person, your own face will take on a bad expression. But if you think of it as a "bad thing" on the premise that all men possess the precious buddha nature, then your countenance will not become bad. On the contrary, it will become a bright face beaming with good will. One cannot help but feel good will toward another who shows good will toward him. Even though you do not meet face to face, mind and mind will communicate. Something in the mind always shows in the action, so the other party is bound to feel it.

You are the one that receives the most benefit when you interpret things with an open mind and good faith. One could even go so far as to say that you do so not for others but for your own sake. That your blood starts to become impure the instant you think there is bad in the outer world, is already proven by scientific tests. There are many cases of sick people showing improvement when they are led to become reconciled with other. This is true not only in relationships between men but also in all aspects of human life. This does not mean we should be unaware of the existence of evil, but that we should not think of evil as a reality. In fact, as one's understanding of the principle of conditionedness becomes clearer, one's understanding of bad habits, of man's shortcomings and the evils of society also becomes clearer, just as if seen through a microscope. But there is no reason one's own blood must be muddied because of that evil. To interpret with good faith does not mean we become unable to see evil. It means, rather, that we see more and more clearly as our mind becomes brighter and brighter.

*Action aggregate and subconscious aggregate.* When we bump up against something bad the encounter can become an opportunity to make our minds brighter. If there were no evil, there would be less chance of our having this blessed opportunity. When we learn to ski, the difficult slope develops our skill and gives us the joy of becoming more dexterous. If unpleasantness develops at the office between you and your superior or you and your fellow workers, making you want to resign, why not first test the power of the principle of conditionedness? Just imagine you have become a skier on the way of human life, and push off with a spirited yell. On the way home from the office, concentrate on "praying to the buddha nature." The next morning, when you arrive at the office, someone calls out, "Good morning." You turn toward the voice wondering who it is, and it turns out to be the associate you had thought of as the cause of bad feeling. Man seems to be stolid, but he is sensitive. It can be said that during the night, while you were sleeping, a wireless was connected to the other party and good intent has been accumulating in his storage battery. Praying to another first brightens one's self, then brightens the other party, and next reflects back on you, making you even brighter.

This feature of acting in relation to the reflection that enters one's mind from the outer world, thus creating a more livable world, Buddha called the "action aggregate." This refers to our physical actions, our deeds, and our thoughts—these three. It also implies that all such actions invariably attach themselves to the subconscious mind and become one's personal possession for eternity. This is the meaning of the "subconscious aggregate."

There is never any end to an action. Without fail, it becomes recorded in the mind and preserved forever. A piano teacher can play just as beautifully whether with eyes open or blindfolded. That practice makes perfect is proof that man's actions are stored in his mind. An acquaintance had a child that was acclaimed a violin virtuoso. Being an only child, the parents emptied their wallets to have him study under someone they thought was the best teacher, but he never reached the world's stages. Later, I heard that the teacher had formed a bad habit in the way he himself played and that the child had copied him. It is said that unless a canary is placed close to a canary that sings beautifully, he will never be of much value. Different parts of a country have different accents. Once this drawl or twang becomes a part of you, it is hard to get rid of.

Whether for good or ill, all actions become a part of you. If for the bad, this is unfortunate, but if for the good, nothing can be better. For if good becomes a part of you, then without any effort good will comes out of you. Like money saved in a bank, you can use it later on.

*Realizing that everything is a reflection of the mind.* A man's actions not only directly improve life but become affixed to his subconscious, taking root and becoming the determinative factor in his next actions. We can understand, therefore, that action and the subconscious are interrelated, having mutual control over each other. One knows he should interpret matters with good faith, but the next instant it changes to ill will. Knowing cigarettes are bad, he lights one the next instant—this is because of his subconsciousness. Buddha called this "karma."

There must be many people who think or say, "It was because of you that this happened." One might put to such people the question, "Will the problem be solved by placing the blame on the other party?"

"No, but this is because the other party does not think as I do."

If this continues, a solution will never be found. The more one argues, the more difficult it will become.

"Are you sure you really want to solve the problem?"

"Of course, I'm sure."

"Then why don't you try to change your own self. If the other party will not change, then there is no way but for you to change."

The reason for blaming someone else is that the subconscious does not want to have the problem solved. In other words, "self-hatred" has found lodging in the mind. One reason some sick persons never seem to improve is that they do not want to lose their extraterritorial right of having others wait on them.

If man only has the will, he can produce as much power as he wants. This is because man by nature possesses "unlimited freedom." When this is understood, there is no need to point the finger of blame at another. Instead, one will promptly change his own attitude. As a result of his decision to change "unlimited freedom" flows from his actions, becoming a power that cannot help but move the other. During a flood, even a huge object is easily washed away. The law of the mind is very similar to the law governing water flow. Being unable to influence another means that your resolution, "It is my fault," is weak.

A problem that long seemed impossible to solve because another was blamed, suddenly starts to unravel the instant one understands and comes to the decision, "I was not making full use of my mind power. This was a reflection of my state of mind."

A self awakening to man's unlimited power, a self reflecting that its full potential has not been developed, is the basic reason for Buddha's teaching of "mind-only," meaning "Everything is a reflection of one's own state of mind." In short, when man comprehends "Everything is a reflection of my mind," he becomes that much more a man. His mind is that much more at ease, and that much more true power surges forth, so there is no problem that cannot be solved.

## WAY OF VIRTUE

*How to love one's wife.* A human being consists, in effect, of two persons: his conscious person and his subconscious person. There are times when the subconscious agrees with the conscious, and times when the conscious must comply with the subconscious. To make the subconscious conform in all respects to the surface consciousness, the subconscious must be made pliant.

In the *Sujata Sutra* (*Singālovāda-sutta*), Buddha sets forth five ways of treating one's wife.

1. Respect your wife.
2. Love your wife.
3. Make your wife feel fulfilled as a woman.
4. Entrust the family finances to your wife.
5. Occasionally buy her gifts of clothes and jewelry.

That is the kind of man Buddha was! There is a thoroughness in these injunctions not even imaginable to bachelor saints. I am sure no woman will be offended by them, nor will any man complain. By always bearing these precepts in mind, a husband can certainly expect the full cooperation of his wife. But to make his own subconsciousness pliant, a similar endeavor is necessary.

1. Practice kindness toward others.
2. Make the body truly healthy.
3. Meditate.
4. Know that you are a god.
5. Have faith.

This is a modern version of the three approaches taught by Buddha as his "hard-and-fast rules for ascetic practice," namely, precept, meditation, and wisdom. To make the subconsciousness a pliant partner, these five injunctions must be practiced daily. Without cultivating a pliant subconscious, you cannot expect it to act according to your desires. Why does the subconscious become pliant when these five injunctions are practiced? Because it sings out in "self-blessing." A feeling of being happy with one's self springs forth, as a result of which the subconscious goes along happily with all the desires of consciousness.

When behavior running contrary to this is practiced, the subconscious falls into a state of "self-hatred." Dangerous feelings will permeate it, such as wanting to commit suicide. These dangerous feelings can also be classified under the heading of "self-punishment." The reason man has such difficulty in attaining the happiness he so desires is that he harbors this emotion of "self-punishment." Man tries to see the good points in others, but when he sums up what he says about them, the criticisms outweigh the rest. Man wants to think, "It is my fault," but this soon changes into, "It is your fault." These are all manifestations of the desire for self-punishment. The prime initiator of this desire to make one's self unhappy lodges in the subconscious.

*The way to make truth a reality.* If one wants to become happy, he must practice the five injunctions. A beginner's subconscious, however, will declare, "It is impossible to practice such a bothersome teaching." Yet the saints of old resolutely carried on the battle until victory was attained. Behind their success was hidden a secret, best expressed in the words of the *Lotus Sutra*, "The years since I attained Buddhahood are immeasurable and boundless."

Coming to the realization "I am forever a practitioner" is the secret to actualizing the truth. To be a practitioner of the truth means to have been a practitioner of the truth from the infinite past. Consequently, no matter how unlimited the deep, many-layered consciousness may be, the virtues of practicing the truth have saturated it in every nook and cranny. Throughout the whole realm of the subconscious, a chorus of "self-blessing" resounds. We are self-blessed from the beginning. To awaken to this is to understand the wisdom of practice.

If you think something is going to be difficult, it proves difficult. If you think it will be easy, it becomes easy. When you climb a high cliff, the legs tremble and you think you might fall. The more you dwell on it, the more dangerous it gets. But as soon as you tell yourself "I am safe," strangely enough the legs stop trembling. In psychology this is called the power of suggestion. "I am forever a practitioner" is also a suggestion. It is "wisdom for practice" given to make difficult self-training easier. Buddha himself discovered this "wisdom of practice" and by putting it to use became the greatest practitioner in the world.

## WAY OF FAITH

*Oneness of seeking enlightenment in one's own strength and in the strength of an Other.*
"I have been a virtuous person since the infinite past." Discovery of this truth blows away the auto-suggestion that this is "difficult to practice" and, like a great elephant walking imposingly across a field, it is the secret that can turn you into a composed practitioner. Just close your eyes and recite three times, "I am buddha from the eternal past." You will get an inkling of the taste of this actual power. And unknowingly, in reality, you may have become a practitioner. Just as the train you board carries you along at a comfortable speed without any special effort, you will speedily become a practitioner of the truth. And even if you do not go out of your way to add the auto-suggestion, "I am a buddha from the eternal past," you are bound to discover yourself naturally becoming so.

When you progress to this great state, a phantasmal thing may appear before your eyes. "Is it a phantom?" No, it is not. This "phantom" will gradually take on more distinct features and stand before you as vividly as your own palms. What is this? It is an experience I hope you can have, for without a personal experience, it is difficult to understand. But in a provisional way, I will describe my own experience.

In the beginning I used to engage in various self-training practices with the thought, "I am an eternal buddha." Then I became aware of another Buddha, far more beautiful than the eternal buddha pictured in my mind, walking in front of me. I had been confident that it would be impossible for a buddha more magnificent than the "Eternal Buddha" within my mind to exist in this universe, but the One before me was certainly much superior. I quickened my pace and approached that beautiful Buddha, and asked him who he was. Then that Buddha turned around, and looked gently but straight at me as if to tell me to look into his eyes.

"Father!" I cried out to my own surprise. I had found my own "Father" for the first time. The Father held my hand firmly in his own and spoke to me, saying, "You are a fine son."

*Attaining the absolute power of an Other.* They say that in the world of art the more one's skill increases, the more clearly an ideal image stands out clearly before the artist's eyes. One makes great progress, but he can never overtake the ideal image that so greatly surpasses his own state. As skill advances, the ideal image becomes so vivid, so faultless, that one becomes ashamed of his state, perhaps breaking his brush in two or smashing his violin. The death of Mr. Yasunari Kawabata, winner of the Nobel Prize for literature, seems similar to this.

The route we follow on Buddha's way is like this, too. The more one advances, the more visibly and vividly do we sense an ideal image in a far higher state of beauty and perfection than we have attained. For every forward step we take, we become conscious that the ideal image has advanced two steps. This is the point at which the world of *faith* suddenly develops. You encounter a "person altogether superior," and before him you feel impelled, against all inner resistance, to bow down. This, I believe, was St. Shinran's position when he affirmed the "absolute power of an Other."

No matter how magnificent your conscious-buddha may be, the more earnest you become, the more clearly you will understand the existence of an "infinitely higher Buddha" whom you cannot possibly equal. When you enter this mental state, then your "self buddha" is no longer a measure for comparison.

You cannot help thinking, "I believed I had opened the eyes of my mind and attained enlightenment by myself, but it was not so. Buddha, the Father, existed before me, and bestowed this enlightenment upon me."

"I walk with the Father Buddha leading me by the hand"—this is surely the sublime culmination of faith. When you come to this point, even as you say, "I am an eternal buddha," you become aware that you are only lip reading, reciting words that Buddha the Father is preaching. There is no effort here. Just as a child learns words by imitating his mother's sounds and lip movements, so we learn that all our enlightenment is a blessing granted to us by our Father Buddha.

Where there is strain, there is fatigue. If one holds a sword tightly, in no time at all he is spent. Someone once asked Shimizu Jirōchō, a famous Japanese swordsman, "You have engaged in over 200 battles, but haven't lost one yet. What is the secret of your strength?"

Jirōchō is said to have laughingly replied, "I am always careful to hold my sword loosely. I approach my opponent and feel out his sword tip with my own. If the tip of his sword is stiff and doesn't move, that's sign he is weaker than I; so I fight him. But if the tip of his sword is flexible and moves easily, I figure he is stronger, and I run away at full speed. Against weaker men I fight, but when it comes to stronger ones, I just glare at them and clear out. That is why I never lose."

If a man is stiff and rigid, he cannot last long. This is the reason for the birth of the expression, the "absolute power of an Other." Buddha too had faith in the absolute power of the Other. There was not an ounce of strain.

# The Way of the Practice of Love

*Love the container, practice the contents.*   Man's happiness is in direct proportion to the "feeling of freedom and love." Consequently, people who want to become happy should pour these feelings into the subconscious. This is the reason for pairing "self-training" and "the practice of love for others." It is much like working hard in order to build up savings for a more secure life. This is what is meant by accumulating "merits."

There is a reason for taking the practice of love first and self-training later. The degree of one's awareness of the "self as buddha" determines the degree of love and respect one feels toward other men. In order to feel a high standard of love, the "degree of self-awareness" must be elevated. But in order to deepen the "degree of self-awareness," the practice of love must come first. If the practice of love is insufficient, the sense of "self-blessing" within the subconscious decreases, and when self-blessing becomes insufficient, whether one sits down to meditate or recite the mantra, whatever he does is ineffective. This is because "self-hatred" creeps into the subconscious and starts a rebellion against the self. Without love, man is instinctively unable to feel the sense of self-blessing. One practices love to perfect "self-awareness" and with the elevation of the degree of self-awareness, he learns the right way to practice love. This is why the sutra teaches: "Love is like a receptacle, practice like water."

Love will progress without self-training, but to train the self without love is to enter a dead end street. To put it in a nutshell, "A self-centered person can never attain enlightenment."

*Four essentials in the quality of love.*   There are four aspects to consider in measuring the quality of love: loftiness, breadth, delicacy, and openness to the love others feel for you.

A lofty love is not like the love shown in stroking a cat's head, but is a love filled with respect. They say a couple must be loving, but if they have nothing but love for each other, their marriage will invariably end in failure. Buddha warned us about this, and taught that besides love, you must "respect your wife." No woman feels displeasure when shown respect. When a sprinkling of respect is expressed in the love, a wife's face will show the greatest satisfaction. Many books on how to make love have appeared in recent years, but love that does not contain respect will soon begin to rot. Buddha elevated this important respect to the highest degree and taught it as "adoration of the Buddha-nature."

To love broadly means to love not only all mankind but also all living and nonliving things, for each and every one possess equally the beautiful buddha-nature. And when they are all, without exception, loved and respected, Buddhism's love is fulfilled. There is not a man on earth who will not rejoice at the veneration of his buddha-nature. This applies not only to the human world but also to animals and even insects. When a dog is loved, he will wag his tail to show pleasure, but when respect is included, the tail will wag furiously in joy. Why not try it out? All animals can sense what is in man's mind. And not only animals but plants as well. On the outskirts of San Francisco, there is a man known for his roses. He is famous for the many improved hybrids he has grown, one of which is a thornless rose. When asked the secret of his success, he answered, "I think it's because I talk to them. The thornless one, everyday I asked it to get rid of the thorns because they were painful." Every morning when he goes out to the garden, he greets all the roses with a cheery "Good morning! And how are you today?" Even roses have a heart. Yet it is not only living things that can sense man's feelings. Even objects considered inanimate by man, objects such as cars, furniture, brushes, and needles, can sense man's feelings. When you buy a car formerly owned by a restless person, the car runs erratically. When you visit a home where the couple is forever quarrelling, the furniture has an annoyed look. If you use a paint brush used by an unskilled person, the brush does not move smoothly; the same is true of needles. On the other hand, if one always expresses gratitude and respect toward cars and brushes, their attitude changes. They start working with the feeling, "I must not betray this master's expectations." The cars themselves will be on the alert, so there is less chance of an accident. In an earlier day in Japan, they built "brush mounds" and "needle mounds" and conducted memorial services for worn-out brushes and needles. This is not because they were primitive but because their instincts were sharp. If you find this hard to believe, conduct your own experiment. Pat your car on the hood and say, "Thank you." Hold an honest attitude like a scientist, and observe the car's reaction.

To love with delicacy means to start by loving those most important to you, leaving others for later. Even the sun, which is supposed to love all things equally, warms things closer to it more intensely, and things far away with less warmth. This is the nature of love. Without being able to love the members of your own family, who are supposedly the closest to you, how can you presume to have neighborly love, or any other kind of love for that matter? To make the excuse that love should be extended to all mankind is useless. Such a love would be of no more value than a shriveled potato. A couple's love is very important, but when compared to the love between parent and child, it has to be recognized as farther from the center. The love of a parent for its child is many times stronger than the love of a couple for one another. To betray the love between parent and child on the ground of love for one's wife or some other pretext would be quite wrong. This would be exactly as if a man were to forget his wife and become engrossed with mistresses. To love his wife, and with her full consent to have a mistress, is quite alright. In the same way, to love one's parents, and at their wish to establish a separate residence, is a true state of married love. One who cannot love his parents, whom he should love the most, can by no means truly love his wife. This would be like trying to construct a two-story building without a first floor.

To sense the love of others is essential because love by nature involves loving and being loved. The joys of love will not be fulfilled on a one-way street. A love that brings joy only to one and not to the other, will end in a break-up. The joy of loving is splendid, but it must go on and attain to the joy of being loved.

"I love all, and all love me." This is the ultimate of love. St. Dōgen called this "the state of being approved by everything." By revering the buddha-nature in each person and thing in the universe, you find that they in turn simultaneously revere the buddha-nature in you. This is the state St. Dōgen was talking about. Not only loving others but discovering in addition that one is loved by others—this is the consummation of love.

I have divided the way of the practice of love into four parts; repentance, gratitude, self-restraint, and rendering love. When "I am sorry," "Thank you," "I will not," and "I will help" all work together, the person involved may accumulate the merits of true love. Repentance and gratitude are inner acts, self-restraint and rendering love outer actions. The first two concern good and bad as they impinge on one from outside, and the latter two concern the good and bad that come from within. As before, this typology includes three yin-yang pairs and conforms to the "principle of the four limbs."

## REPENTANCE

*Principle of forgiveness.* Even when I was young, I thought the virtue of magnanimity very important.

Buddha said, "If you return malice with malice, malice will never end. If you return malice with forgiveness, malice will disappear and peace will be gained."

Jesus too, in reply to a question about how often one should offer forgiveness, declared, "I do not say seven times; I say seventy times seven."

How difficult it is to truly forgive. But when we comprehend, in accordance with the principle of conditionedness, that man does not act of his own free will but behaves as he does because of preceding conditions, then we see that it is easy to forgive others. This discovery so delighted me that I named the principle of conditionedness the "forgiveness principle" and taught it as such to others.

"When a car hits a telephone pole, it does no good to blame it, kick it, or hold a grudge against it."

I explained how irrational it is to blame others. Some were quick to understand, and easily set aside grudges they had carried for years. There is no question that this truth saves those who forgive as well as those who are forgiven. But there is more to it than this.

*Magnanimity not a virtue.* Suppose that a man has been carrying around a burden of ill-will for many years. Even if he were now to forgive the other, the wound in his mind would not heal completely. Also, the person who incurred the ill-will comes off a loser. If the grudge was the result of a mistake, it might even become the basis of a claim for compensation. In many cases, misunderstandings give rise to grievances. So even though you may forgive someone in your heart, this does not solve the matter. That is why we need "repentance." It is not "I forgive *him*" but "I am truly sorry. Without reason I felt bitter toward you and caused you unhappiness. Please forgive *me*." This is repentance. "Forgetting that you possess buddha-nature, I held ill-will toward you. I feel truly repentant." When you talk thus in your mind, true forgiveness is brought about, and the harm that resulted is done away with both in yourself and in the other party.

Illuminated by the rays of Buddha's truth, the bearer of a grudge already sees that he is in the wrong, so it is easy for him to forgive. Unless, however, he repents of the mistaken way of thinking he harbored for so long, he will continue to act contrary to the way of love. But when you say "I'm sorry" and repent when you do wrong, the other party feels happy, and there is less chance of your repeating the wrong. This is such a commonplace thing that there is no need to elaborate. But there is a tendency in society to regard as a virtue the magnanimity that leads to forgiveness. Such arrogance can by no means be considered a virtue. What is commonly considered the virtue of "magnanimity" toward other's wrongdoing is better described as a virtue when it is called "penitence."

## GRATITUDE

*One cause of bizarre social movements.*   Love is not complete without the combined feelings of loving and being loved. Many are so absorbed in helping others that they are not aware of the love given to them. They are lacking in feeling.

When I was still a student, there was a dog named Hachiko always sitting in front of Shibuya Station in Tokyo. It seems that his master had passed away suddenly, and Hachiko, unable to understand this, waited many years for his master to come through the ticket gate. After a long and lonely wait, he died in front of the station. The deeply touched station employees and commuters built a statue in memory of "Hachiko the Loyal Dog." If there had not been a strong reason for doing so, a dog, whose nature it is to run and frisk about, could not possibly sit in one spot for years, sometimes even forgetting to eat. In other words, he could not have endured the hardship and agony without a certain "joy" in doing it. This is the joy of "sensing the love of another." In days gone by, it used to be called the "debt of gratitude." Gratitude should be part of us at all times, but it seems to be a word lost on the present generation.

Children who grow up without learning to be grateful are certainly to be pitied. They suffer from a severe "love deficiency," and from an instinctive desire to compensate for it may wind up insane or throw themselves into radical social movements. Man is an animal that cannot live without love. Therefore, when he feels a lack of it, he unconsciously seeks substitute. A social movement may be a wonderful thing, but if it erupts fitfully from a "love deficiency," then it is not good. A man who has gone without food for two weeks and is starving will devour food the instant he sees it. This is human nature, but a life lived fitfully usually ends tragically.

*Four objects of gratitude : parents, country, society, and the Three Treasures.*   When Buddha teaches indebtedess, he lifts up four main points: the gratitude we owe our parents, the gratitude we owe our country, the gratitude we owe society, and the gratitude we owe for the Three Treasures. The sequence takes us from the small to the large, but as a means for bringing the entire panorama of gratitude into view, these four aspects are invaluable.

A mother's love is always at work, even when we are unaware of it. As an example of constant, never-ending love, there is nothing to surpass it. But the value of a parent's love goes deeper, for it is an "absolutely trusting love." Even though she knows her child has done wrong, the mother will trust him. She separates the incident from the person completely, and trusts to the very end in what is beautiful and good in him. This is a natural instinct, but this motherly instinct is of exactly the same nature as that of Buddha's act of "adoring the buddha-nature." Therein lies hidden the indestructible value of parental love. A child who grows up receiving this parental love cannot help but sense it at some time or another. Despite the dissoluteness of this world, man has surprisingly retained his humanity. I believe this is largely due to the power of parental instinct in trusting children unconditionally.

In recent years, many homes do not trouble to fly the national flag. This must be remedied. How many hundreds and thousands of precious lives have been sacrificed for this country? To be unable to feel this invaluable love is a pitiful thing. It is because of the many thousands of people who, in times past, worked daily for the sake of this country that we now live in peace. This treasure is not something found lying by chance on the roadside. To be so insensitive as to treat it with neglect would be to cut off one means of knowing man's kindness. What would be left, even though it might look human, would be like making the mind live in the dark solitary cell of a prison. "Love deficiency symptoms" will arise within the subconscious and eventually lead to alcohol, smoking, drugs, and other forms of self-deception.

A teacher once told me he does not raise the stars and stripes because a strong spirit of nationalism will lead to war. Does he think a strong family consciousness makes a person a bad member of society? The stronger one's family consciousness, the deeper his respect for other families. As one's spirit of appreciation for his country increases, will it not create a deeper regard for other nations? We must not overlook the social law: "Only he who respects himself can respect others."

At any rate, on national holidays let us raise the flag and express our appreciation to past leaders of the nation. Let us respect and cherish the flag, remembering the many who died for it. If the next generation were to growup beholding the beautiful sight of a flag fluttering from every housetop, they would become children deeply rooted in love. It is not just Buddha or Christ we should be thankful for. Without a country, of what purpose is Buddha or Christ?

That we are able to live with such a high standard of free and cultured life is a blessing we owe mankind. We can ride on a bus and go visit a friend only because the bus exists and the road is there. The bus or the road did not just happen to be there. They are gifts to us, results of mans' efforts. "That's mutual," someone may say. Indeed it is. So why don't we mutually say, "Thank you"?

One fellow thinks, "I work to earn money," and looks at other people the same way. What stupidity! When jobs are there as situations from which we can help each other, it is demeaning to think of them as money-making opportunities. If we have to work anyway, why not work with a good feeling? "That's true," I'm sure you will reply. Then why can't you think, "I am being given the opportunity to work to help others." It is a sociological fact that man is always working for others. A baker bakes goodies not so he himself can eat them but so others can eat them. Any work, without exception, follows this "law of mutual help." If this is a scientific truth, there is no reason we should not say "Thank you" to each other. If only the seller said, "Thank you," and the buyer took it for granted that he should be thanked, this would be a form of mental illness, for such thinking is topsy-turvy.

If you work all day with the feeling that you are serving others, the work premises become a "place of love." What a pleasant feeling! Just try it. And as a result, work efficiency will climb and income increase. If the prayer "May everyone who uses this product become happy" is included and shipped out to the markets, the consumers will be wrapped in that love melody and will become happy. All objects receive and store the melody and will become happy. All objects receive and store the mind waves of man. The beauty of a Japanese sword is not simply in its craftmanship. Its beauty derives from the fact that the forge is first purified, and the sword forged with fervent repetitions of the prayer "Peace on earth." All objects possess a mind befitting their form. All objects are alive.

Gratitude for the Three Treasures means gratitude for Buddha's love, for the love of the universe, and for the love of the person who teaches us of them. Because of the appearance of great saints, man can live as he should, in peace. If religion had not come to exist in this world, it might have become a world of wild beasts. It is due to the efforts and sufferings of the saints that men have learned how to become human, how to live without fighting tooth and claw. Those born as men must be aware of this important fact. When a man understands the love of the saints, then for the first time he can comprehend the highest love. And indeed, by being embraced in this never-ending love, his "hunger and thirst for love" should be completely satisfied.

Universal love is represented by the sun, air, water, and earth. When heaven and earth are made the two determinative categories, sun and air are considered heaven, and water and soil are considered earth. These four comprise the fundamental conditions that must be present for life to exist. If even one of them is lacking, instant death is inevitable. Everyone seems to know the great importance of these elements, but how many sense that they are expressions of "love"? One youth said, "My parents brought me into this world quite arbitrarily and raised me on their own. I don't owe them a thing." This is true, but "My parents are always concerned about me" is also true. Then which of these should I adopt in order to become happy? Let us think honestly. There is no doubt that heaven and earth exist naturally. From this perspective there is no need to feel appreciation. On the other hand, everytime we look at the sun, we give thanks. Whenever we drink water, we feel gratitude. Which makes for a happier life, to live feeling this love every second, or to live without feeling it? I think that for establishing a place for the practice of love, nothing is more thorough than to look at the way of the universe. The sun keeps sending us warm rays, and the air, water, and soil also, though polluted by man, continuously keep up the effort of purifying themselves and serve mankind. This diligent effort cannot be equaled by anyone. A polluted heaven and earth purifies itself to protect mankind. Keeping that thought in mind and living with gratitude costs nothing. Why not, then, offer your feeling of appreciation to the sun and water? Then the effect of the sun's rays on you will change. The way the water you drink works as it goes through your body from mouth to stomach and intestines will change. This is not merely because of the change in your way of feeling. Practice and experience it.

In this manner, you will begin to understand that these four aspects symbolize God in his permeation of the universe—and that you are enfolded and protected right in the midst of it. I worship these four as messengers of God.

*Spirit of flower arrangement.* In a flower arrangement there are traditionally three main stems: the tallest, called "heaven," the shortest, called "earth," and the one in the middle, called "man." Man, enfolded between heaven, with its sun and air, and earth, with its water and soil, is loved and protected by them. If there are any teachers who have forgotten this important point, I wish they would pause here and consider anew the true spirit of flower arrangement. A flower symbolizes in a single form the accumulated blessings of heaven and earth. To look at a flower is to see one's self. We arrange flowers, indeed, to attain the enlightenment that our true aspect is as beautiful as the flower. Therefore, just before we begin an arrangement, we must think that we are about to receive Buddha's teaching, and bow our heads. This is equally true of the tea ceremony.

It is only natural that we should express gratitude to those people who teach us of the blessings of Buddha, and also of heaven and earth. Prince Shotoku said, "The Three Treasures are the Buddha, the dharma, and the masters." For men they are, literally, three treasures.

## SELF-RESTRAINT

*Spirit of the five precepts.* Buddha taught, as something that all should observe, the Five Precepts: do not kill, do not steal, do not commit adultery, do not tell lies, and do not drink intoxicants. These five were subdivided in minute detail and exactness. First there was an increase from 5 to 10, then from 10 to 250, later from 250 to 500—until now we have a voluminous sutra full of precepts. But it all boils down to one sentence: "Do not cause trouble for others." "Do not" may sound very rigid to some people, but when you understand the sentence to mean "you are not to bother other people," it becomes a simple and clear teaching.

There are today more than a few people who strive to help others through charity projects and social movements, but there is one thing I cannot understand about them. At a gathering where a charity project was being discussed, some sat coolly smoking cigarettes. Their attitude was so haughty I could not help but say, "Your charitableness is appreciated, but please stop smoking in public." It is common knowledge now that there are quite a few who are disturbed by or even allergic to cigarette smoke.

*A word to young people participating in social movements.* Some young people are so brazen as to declare, "In order to bring about social reform, we must place time bombs in the Capitol." Such people are no different from the aforementioned charity workers. They seem to be imitating the idea that guides a doctor when he performs surgery, "For the sake of the whole, we have to cut away a part."

"But do you realize," you who hold this idea, "that to do something to another is to have something done to yourself?" Have you ever considered that any person can be "one's self" and that one's self can be "another"? You have your own standpoint and reasons, and so does the other person. You do not respect others because you can not respect your own self. When you respect yourself, then you will always respect others. When a person who cannot even respect himself talks of social reform, society suffers. First elevate yourself to a state where you can truly respect yourself. That is where correct social reform begins.

"Why do you say I do not respect myself?"

"Your breathing is shallow. People who have respect for themselves breathe deeply. Your chin juts out, your pelvic bones jut forward, and your shoulder is twisted. People who are not confident of their self-worth are all the same."

"Then what can I do to be able to respect myself?"

"First of all, be kind to your parents. Do things that will make your parents happy and grateful. Extend your kindness to the rest of the family, then to the neighbors. Small kindnesses are quite alright. Do things that will make others want to thank you. In addition, if your blood is impure, your thinking won't be straight, so be careful of your diet. Eat foods that contain varieties of vitamins and minerals, especially calcium. Practice "meditation" and correct your posture and breathing. Then study the truth of the universe. Come to my place for one week, and at the end of that time you will notice a complete change in your posture and facial expression. Your head will become clear and lucid, and you will be able to tell the best way to reform society."

Young people who have no consideration for others always have crooked backs. This affects the brain, and they become so absorbed in criticizing society that their brain is weakened to the point where they cannot criticize themselves. When the leaders of a nation become aware of the truth that mens' thoughts are decided by breathing, food, and posture, then their ideas for producing worthy people will be on the right track.

BESTOWING LOVE

*Kindness from within.*   Buddha teaches that the way of helping others involves helpfulness of four kinds: from the mind, through our words, through our deeds, and through our work. When these four are combined, the way of helping others is brought to fulfilment. The degree to which one practices the way of love determines the degree of one's self-blessing. The degree of one's self-blessing determines the effectiveness of his self-training. Consequently, it is necessary to attend carefully to what perfect practice of the way of love entails.

Kindness from within and kindness through words both belong to mental kindness, while kindness through deeds and kindness through occupation have to do with physical kindness. Even to help one's self, one necessarily relies on both the mental and physical. So too when we assist someone else, both mental and physical kindness must be present if it is to be kindness worth the name.

To help with the mind means to lend a helping hand for the sake of another's happiness with prayer. When a child is riding unsteadily on a bicycle, you think "Don't get hurt." This is a prayer. Or in accordance with the law of the mind, you concentrate your strength in the *tanden* and pray, "He will not get hurt." This is more effective. Mind and mind always sense each other.

There are times when a man desires a small kindness, and times when he wants a big kindness. Even when driving on a busy street, you can tell clearly which cars are being driven by kind persons and which are not. The kindnesses exhibited in this situation are usually small kindnesses, but when one is driving on a lonely country road and the car breaks down, then a big kindness becomes necessary. In any case a kindness is a kindness, whether big or small, so let us never overlook the small kindnesses.

*Kindness in word and proper giving.* There are many ways of expressing kindness through words. Saying "Good morning" to a stranger on the street, telling jokes to make people laugh, or praising a person's good points behind his back. Big or small, opportunities for kindness in word exist everywhere.

Yet even though opportunities for inner kindnesses and verbal kindnesses, big and small, are found every moment, whatever the form of a kindness, its ultimate end should be to "manifest the buddha-nature." When a kindness is based on the prayer that peoples' buddha-nature will become manifest, then it can indeed be called a "genuine kindness." It must not be mere "pampering kindness" or "annoying kindness." Indulgent love or pampering affection is most frequent among parents, and annoying love is found most often among religious professionals.

Buddha's compassion is still felt deeply in our hearts today because his was a kindness to reveal our buddha-natures. No kindness in the world is more precious than the sublime kindness of revealing the buddha-nature. As long as one lives conscious of his buddha-nature, he need never feel impoverished at any time or any place. Just as Aladdin's lamp brought forth treasure after treasure, so one who lives in awareness of his buddha-nature will find that all things necessary to life are his. So whatever sort of kindness you may do, make certain that a prayer for "revealing the buddha-nature" is always included. Even a parent's love for a child, if not accompanied by some manifestation of buddha-nature, can only be described as a poor love. If a parent prays for continued happiness for the child even after he is gone, this, more than anything else, will teach the child the preciousness of buddha-nature.

This holds true for anyone, and sincere practice of the way of love will always develop into a concrete form of action to reveal the buddha-nature. Even today packages intended for Buddhist priests have written on them the word "offering," meaning that they are offered as a form of action for the revealing of the buddha-nature. To request the services of a full-time Buddhist disciple in the hope of accumulating great merit in the practice of love is like investing in good stocks in the hope of reaping a great profit. One must first ascertain the quality of the priest; otherwise he may suffer great damage instead of earning great merit.

*Physical kindness and kindness through one's occupation.* Physical practice of the way of love contrasts with helping others from within. Buddha simply divided this into love as practiced through bodily movement and love as practiced through one's work, but these two must be practiced together as a complementary pair. Acts of love, such as picking up dangerous articles you find lying on the ground, may at times be stopped in mid-course because of an aching back. To prevent this kind of thing from stopping you, I shall make two suggestions. The first is to learn Yoga exercises in such a way that when you bend over to pick things up, you will bend so as to bring about improvement in your back. Those who think they are too busy to spare the time to pick up an object, can make up the time through the Yoga exercise of "long strides." When massaging or pounding another's stiff shoulders, learn to utilize that motion to relax your own. Yoga exercise teaches such body carriage. The other suggestion is to think of yourself as a third person watching yourself perform acts of love. Try to listen to a voice praising you and saying, "You are accumulating secret virtue." When you start to think in this manner, surprisingly enough, good acts that once seemed irksome become easy to do.

Practice of love through one's occupation means that regardless of what your work may be, there is always something you can do through it to increase man's happiness. While earning money, practice the way of love and earn "virtue." This is double profit, so the work becomes more enjoyable. People who think, "How can I be of more help to others," have such happy faces that others always sense something. So one is impressed with "that store," with "that company," or with "that teacher." They say "service is the best trademark." Anyone can readily discover the truth of this motto.

In the practice of love through one's occupation there is yet another important point. This is the practice of love in the use of money. "I am able to work like this because of many people's kindness. Because I am enfolded in their love, I am able to work profitably. I must offer part of that profit, whenever an opportunity arises, for the sake of man's happiness." That is it in a nutshell. There are some pitiful people too tight to give away even the dust that gets into their eyes. The purpose of a fortune is simply to satisfy man's instinctive desire for freedom. If "freedom" has been attained, it is better not to have a fortune. Life's journey is more enjoyable when your body is light. As long as you have enough for necessities, it is better not to have more. "I have diabetes. Poor people can't have this sickness." I heard these words from the lips of an arrogant man. "For protection I have two German shepherds and in every room a gun." Thus he bragged, but at fifty-six he had a stroke, and after being bedridden for seven years, he passed away. The lighter the load on your shoulders, the happier is life's journey. When one is able to discern this simple rule, he has learned the most important thing.

This concludes the foregoing brief explanation of the way of the practice of love. Have you forgotten to express repentance or appreciation? Do you unwittingly cause trouble to others? Do you give true help to others? The four parts of the explanation are intended solely to help you understand the meaning of perfect love and bring forth the fruit of self-blessing.

# The Way of Self-Training

## UNDERSTANDING THE WAY OF SELF-TRAINING

*Buddhahood as flexibility of body and mind.*   When a feeling of "self-blessing" wells up as a result of practicing the way of love, your self-training will proceed as smoothly as a ski over snow. When self-training seems difficult, it is because you have forgotten to practice love—like trying to ski when there is no snow.

Self-training means to make the truth a part of you. The ability to read music does not make you a piano player. Similarly, knowing the truth does not make you a buddha. By practicing the truth so that it becomes a part of you, you become a buddha and life becomes brighter. In contemporary language, self-training is to make the truth a part of your subconscious.

First, let us ascertain what is meant here by "truth." I call it "flexibility of mind and body." The transcendental truth of the Three Dharma Seals, the creative truth of the Five Aggregates and the 84,000 teachings developed from them,—all seem to terminate in "flexibility of mind and body." And the value of this truth or teaching is determined, it would seem, by the degree of "flexibility of mind and body" that is attained.

"Flexibility of mind and body" means that mind and body alike are to be supple. There is no stiffness anywhere in the body and no rigidity in the mind. The body moves freely, the mind moves freely, and successful blending of the two becomes "unhindered freedom." This is precisely what characterizes a buddha. The words "flexibility of mind and body" are recorded in the *Larger Sukhāvatī-vyūha,* and the saintly priest Dōgen once gave a forceful exposition of these words, even going so far as to speak of "stripping off mind and body."

*Loss of the Three Treasures by Buddhism.*   As explained above, there is a "true way" and an "expedient way" in Buddhism. Beginners are taught the expedient way. If taught the complete truth at once, they would find it difficult to understand and would not practice it. So it is divided into parts and taught. But since it is taught in parts, a situation is created in which people tend to forget the whole. Man has a tendency to remember only things he feels interested in and to reject the rest. Studying a part and becoming imbued with the idea that the part is the whole—this is the state of most contemporary Buddhist denominations. If Buddhists had followed Buddha's spirit of the middle way and not forgotten to learn the whole, the present abominable confrontations between sects could not occur. In future, Buddhists must dissolve their denominations and return to the original, united, harmonious brotherhood, or they cannot truly say they have faith in Buddha. Though great stress is laid on the importance of embracing the Three Traesures—the Buddha, the dharma, and the brotherhood—where is this "harmonious brotherhood" we are supposed to embrace? The slogan that calls for "conversion to the Three Treasures" involves a grave misrepresentation.

Because they have forgotten how to distinguish between the expedient way and the complete way, today's Buddhists have become, in this respect, morally atrophied. The expedient way as such is not bad, just as it is not bad to have elementary school before high school. But if an elementary school teacher should announce to the pupils, "Do not go on to high school," there would be a problem. The majority of religious professionals commit this mistake. This is why it is important to raise high the banner of "flexibility of mind and body."

If the people belonging to denominations cultivated a "flexible mind" and learned to understand the good points of other religions and denominations, the ugly factions that exist today would disappear. And studying the good points in other groups that your own does not possess will bring you toward the goal of Buddhahood that much faster.

*Buddhism not a way of rigorous ascetic practice.* The mistake of most modern religious groups is that they are overly inclined toward the mind and have forgotten the body. That Buddhism has from the outset been a way of mind and body together becomes clear even from considering the posture of meditation. Moreover, most of the precepts are concerned with teaching good body carriage. To forget this true way and teach that one can become a buddha through mental attitude alone is a grave mistake. People who forget to study the way of the body and concentrate only on the mind can never, no matter how hard they try, attain the state of buddhahood. So long as they do no more than lament "how difficult Buddhism is," there is no particular problem, but when the attitude changes to, "No man can expect to become a buddha—back to ordinary life for me," he falls into the pit of "human vanity." This kind of thing happened even as early as the period of original Buddhism, and the disputes between the Theravada and Mahayana Buddhists are a further manifestation of this. The person who takes this view has failed to become a buddha because he failed to go about it correctly, but arbitrarily decided that all men are like himself.

Buddha established "the way of mind and body in complementary relation" because he perceived that the body relaxes only if the mind is relaxed, and that the mind relaxes only if the body is relaxed. And only when the body-mind relaxation is perfected can "unhindered freedom" be attained. This is the true way of Buddhism, and when you follow this, Buddhism becomes quite easy. I believe there is no action more insulting to the Buddha than to give the impression that "Buddhism is too difficult, far beyond the capability of man." This is like holding up a picket sign at the entrance to Buddhism, "Too difficult. Do not enter." Buddha taught only what is possible to everyone. If only you make your mind and body flexible, you will immediately understand that this is what the state of Buddhahood is like. If you were told to "walk on one foot," then of course it would be a "difficult way." But as soon as you know that you are to "walk with two feet," then you find that it is an exceedingly "easy way." From one foot to two feet—do not make the mistake of thinking that the difference is merely twofold. Because of the "multiplication principle," this change from one foot to two makes walking the Buddhist way many times easier. This is the secret of the Buddhist "way of mind and body in complementary relation."

The aim of the self-training way is to make mind and body pliant. The training naturally divides, therefore, into two aspects. The aspect centered in the use of a mystic formula or mantra has the mind primarily in view. The aspect centered in meditation puts the body at the forefront. In the mantra way, vocalization is central, and this way involves enshrining a symbol of deity. In the meditation way, meditation is central, and this involves purification. Thus the self-training way has four parts: the symbol of deity, the mantra, purification, and meditation. The symbol of deity and mantra form one yin-yang pair, purification and meditation another. Again, the symbol of deity and the mantra on the one hand, and purification and meditation on the other, constitute another yin-yang pair, the three pairs together manifesting the principle of the four limbs.

## THE DIVINE IMAGE

*The divine image in original Buddhism.*   The origin of the divine image lies in Buddha's character. One reason Buddhism spread is of course that the truth its founder taught was so lofty, but an equally important reason is that his character was so noble. The scene of his very first sermon at Deer Park is described in the *Mahāvagga*.

The five companions of his six years of ascetic practices remembered his abandoning such practices and leaving them. They had branded him a "degenerate" and had promised each other to have nothing to do with him. But when Buddha appeared before them, despite their vow, they unconscioulsy bowed low in homage, prepared a seat for him, and washed his feet. When one of them addressed him as "Gautama," Buddha's family name, he admonished them all, saying, "Dear bhikkhus, I am a buddha. You must not call a buddha by name."

From this you can tell how lofty Buddha's personality was. To have Buddha seated in the center of a circle and themselves around him, totally absorbed in his sermon—this was salvation itself to the disciples. Without special training in meditation, the disciples were able to experience a great salvation. Yet even without being personally present at the sermons, but just by picturing him in their minds and worshipping him, some disciples found salvation. Buddha's personality with its pliant mind and body had already made other people's minds and bodies relaxed. This was possible even before a sermon or self-training. This was the source of "the way of the divine image." Many saints have appeared in the world, but as a human whose "personality" was yearned for, none can surpass Buddha. This becomes clear just by looking at the remains of sculptural art in India, China, Japan, or wherever Buddhism has spread. It is amazing that one human being should have been so loved and esteemed.

*Buddha himself the divine image.*   Statues of Buddha were already being carved and venerated while he was still alive. The question thus arises, did Buddha himself engage in worship? Buddhism is always supposed to be a way in which "all members are equal," so if worship is incumbent on us, it stands to reason that it must also have been necessary for Buddha. Concerning this matter, Buddha taught in the *Āgama Sutras*:

"Not to have an object of worship for one's faith is a source of anxiety for man. The truth I awakened to is the same Truth as that which all buddhas from the ancient past worshipped, and which I worship now. Buddhas of the future will doubtless also worship this same Truth. To those desirous of becoming a buddha I say, worship, honor, and serve this Truth."

Buddha's living faith thus becomes vividly clear. By "ancient Buddhas" he meant not only that there are many other planets in this universe inhabited by men, but also that on those planets, in addition to our own, buddhas have appeared and become the "eyes" of mankind. The divine being worshipped with one accord by the countless buddhas of the universe is the same God that Buddha worshipped so reverently.

Again, as Buddha stated concisely in a sutra with the Chinese title *Liao pên shêng ssŭ ching*, Those who see the Truth, see me. Buddha is alive forever in the Truth." This is the reason that instead of Buddha's ashes, a piece of paper with the words "Poem of Truth" written on it is sometimes placed within an urn when a stupa is built.

Buddha directly worshipped the Truth. But Buddha's disciples worshipped Buddha rather than the Truth. The followers would thus seem to be making a mistake as to the divine image, but since Buddha himself has proclaimed that his true body is the Truth, Buddha is a "representative of the Truth," and this makes it very natural to worship the Truth through Buddha. Therefore it can be said that the "divine image" in Buddha's worship of the Truth and that of the disciples' worship of Buddha were essentially the same. The difference between the two corresponds to the difference between respecting one's country directly and respecting it through its national flag. Depending on circumstances, either is quite alright. But to think "In that case a flag is unnecessary" would be a mistake. By the same token, it would also be a mistake to jump to the conclusion that as long as we have the Truth, Buddha is not necessary. For man is an animal that can create an even higher culture through "symbolism."

*Accepting symbolism.*   Animals do not have words or letters. Lacking symbolism in this sense, they have no developed education. The reason man is man is that he quickly learned to utilize symbolic forms and create words and letters. This is the foundation of human civilization today. Therefore, even in the world of religion, symbolism should be widely utilized. This is the basic principle at work in all statues of Buddha and must be acknowledged as the true meaning of all worshipped images in every Buddhist sect. To put it more simply, if you have a significant motto you want to hold before yourself, it will be better for you to write it on paper and hang it on the wall rather than to store it in your mind. If you can understand this, you should also be able to understand why the divine image is adorned and worshipped.

There was a time when the ministers of Christianity looked contemptuously upon the Buddhist divine image as a form of "idol worship." But eventually they became aware that they were worshipping the cross, and now they hardly ever mention the subject.

*The practice of love as glorification of the divine image.*   To adorn an object of worship and symbolize the unseen God is a precious path natural to men. It should be clearly understood, however, that this adornment is not just a matter of pleasing ourselves.

Whether it be a family Buddhist altar or an altar in a temple, half of it is meant as a love practice towards others. To adorn the object of worship in a way identifiable to others is to "give Buddha" to the other's mind.

Though today's Japanese Buddhism could hardly be more stagnant, the temples of Nara and Kyoto attract many tourists. The priests may be dozing, but the throngs come uninvited. Starting with Emperor Shōmu (A.D. 701–756) who built the Temple of the Great Buddha of Nara, why did so many philanthropists build such magnificent temples and Buddha statues? It was not so much to leave indications of their self-training as to cultivate faith in the multitudes. The fact that people are still drawn to them today, a thousand years later, is a testimony to the depth of the practice of love to which the ancient Buddhists devoted themselves. The phrase "temple Buddhism" suggests the derogatory term "absentee priest" which in turn means a "hollow temple," but that these temples are contributing something to enrich the minds of people in todays' world cannot be denied.

To have a Buddhist altar, even a small one, installed in the home is a wonderful thing. It is a restful haven for the elderly, a place of education for children, and a place where the couple can express their love for those who have gone before. The altar should have in the center a divine image clearly symbolizing Truth, and on the step in front of it, a statue of Shakyamuni Buddha should be enshrined. For unless Buddha and the Truth are together, it is hard for people to be content. Man wants to satisfy his intellect as well as his emotions. Truth satisfies the reason and Buddha satisfies the emotions. "Buddha is a symbol of the Truth." This one sentence explains everything.

A word of explanation should be added about the tradition that accompanies the adorning of the object of worship. It is traditional to offer the "three complements" of light, flowers, and incense. The light symbolizes wisdom, the flower compassions, and incense virtue—or, in other words, "freedom, love, and faith." One might use words like these when presenting these offerings:

> In offering the light, I worship the buddha within me,
> With the flower, I worship the buddha within all others,
> And by offering incense, I worship my father Buddha.

Worshipping your own buddha-nature, worshipping the buddha-nature in others, and worshipping Buddha the father—this, I believe, is the whole of Buddhism in a nutshell. That is why these three symbols are called the "three complements." As you face the altar, place the light on the right, the flower on the left, and the incense in the center.

## MANTRA

*Sutra chanting as hearing Buddha's explanation of the dharma.*   Directly connected with worshipping the divine image is the important practice of chanting the mantra. This can be called a reenactment of the joy of listening to the preaching of Buddha. Just as the adornment of the divine image arose naturally from worshipping the Buddha, sutra chanting developed from the "joy of listening to the Truth."

"Truth" exists always and everywhere, but unless it appears in words, it might as well be nonexistent. Buddha's enlightenment was to grasp the Truth of the universe as "words," and preaching is to present the Truth as "words."

When you understand that "Truth has value only when it is in words," then whether it be words within the mind or vocalized words it will be readily understood that great effort must be made to put the Truth into words. This is the reason for the birth of mantra practice.

We should understand that there are two different kinds of mantra. One is an explanatory kind and the other a motto-like type. Most sutras are explanatory. But in addition there are motto-like, short "words" selected for repeated chanting, for example, *Namu Amida butsu*, *Namu Myōhō Renge Kyō*, *Namu Daishi Henjō kongō*, and *Om mani padme hum*. The purpose of the two kinds is different, so I will call the former "sutra chanting" and the latter "incantation." Generally, when one speaks of "mantra," it means "incantation," but properly speaking "sutra chanting" is also mantra. Moreover, there is no harm in calling the words we use in daily life "mantra" if they are "words of truth" that bring about pliancy of mind and body.

The purpose of the scriptures is to explain the Truth, but many sutras are in "poem" style. Both now and in the past, poetry has served one purpose. When man is deeply touched, an impelling desire arises to share that emotion with others. It becomes necessary to entrust this emotion to simple, melodious "words." Poetry is not simply for the purpose of conveying a message but also so that one may recite alone, and others too may recite, thus making it possible to savor the stirring emotions for a long time.

I doubt that Buddha himself wrote and left behind poems, but within the scriptures there are many "Buddha poems." When reading them today, one is struck by their outstanding literary style not to mention the depth of their insight into the nature of truth. Regrettably they are available only in the original or in Chinese translation, so they are not suitable for people of other languages.

At any rate, there are many poems transmitted in the scriptures, poems that anticipate our recitation, but of course the whole of scripture is worthy of recitation, both in terms of literary value and in terms of truth. Sutra chanting is also beneficial to quieting the mind. Even when you are burdened with anxieties, sutra chanting will make you forget them. Though you may not understand the meaning of the scripture, the chanting helps you to recapture serenity. This is because you accept sutra chanting as "Buddha's words." When you sense sutra chanting as listening to "Buddha's explanation of the dharma," then even though you may not understand the words of the sermon, Buddha's virtue will enter your breast. That in itself is an invaluable benefit of sutra chanting. For adorning the divine image and reciting the sutra before it brings to a climax the virtue of the manifestation of Buddha.

*Incantation as a way of self-hypnosis.*   In addition to sutra chanting there is the practice of "incantation." Emphasis is placed on repeated recitation of a very short mantra. This is very effective for concentration of the mind, but the aim is rather to purify the deepest layer of the subconscious. When the same word is repeated over and over, you enter a state of self-hypnosis. Then the deepest layer of the subconsciuos, which usually will not easily open its mouth, opens wide. When the Truth is poured in at that time, it penetrates into the deepest layer of the subconscious, so that even after the incantation has stopped, the Truth keeps working and will determine the man.

I once heard of a Hollywood actor who was afraid to fly in a plane. Because of the nature of his occupation, this frequently caused great inconvenience. He therefore went to a hypnotist and got rid of this phobia. Drinking and smoking habits can also be cured by hypnosis. The subject is led into a hypnotic state, and a suggestion is made. If the suggestion is, "You love to ride on planes," the airplane hater will become an airplane lover, and if it is suggested, "You can't even stand the sight of liquor," he will become a liquor hater. Mans' mind is such that it is easily changed by suggestion.

Incantation is a form of "self-hypnosis." To have another decide what will be suggested to you is in principle not a good thing, though there are doubtless exceptions. The reason it is not good is that it hurts your character. No one wants a robot-like personality. From beginning to end, self-hypnosis acts only in accordance with one's own will, so there is no robot-like tendency. On the contrary, your power of self-control is strengthened, so this should be greatly encouraged. Everyone has experienced at one time or another the difficulty of curing a bad habit. This difficulty is due to weak self-control, but when you study the way of self-hypnosis, this difficult problem can easily be solved. This is what incantation does.

Repetition of the same word is a way of inducing hypnosis, and the word you habitually recite is not some other person's word but the word of Truth itself. So while reciting, you are not only led into a state of hypnosis but are being given a good suggestion where there is no robot-like danger. There is no mistake in saying that the divine image is adorned to correctly guide this "suggestion" so that a more effective result can be obtained. One may even go so far as to say that as long as the enshrined divine image is correct, it does not matter what the incantation word is. The incantation word is used as a means to induce hypnosis, and "suggestion" will be received chiefly from the "object of worship." Indeed, because of this fact, one understands better how important it is to adorn the divine image, and similarly, that it does not matter if we do not know the meaning of the incantation. Chanting incomprehensible words actually speeds the entrance into the state of hypnosis.

Therefore, it is not always necessary to know the meaning of the incantation word. But the object of your worship, the divine image, must become increasingly clear or, like a kite with a broken string, your subconscious will be blown away in directions you can neither predict nor control. Be warned that a grave danger is concealed in the failure to achieve clarity as to the divine image. That there are many mentally disturbed people among incantation practitioners is most unfortunate. Leaders must take heed and be careful.

*Words of mystic power in the practice of love.*   Mantra practice is a way of manifesting the "value of words." This value should be made use of not only in sutra recitation and incantation but also in the words we use in our daily lives. When the words "Good night" are accompanied by the thought, "May Buddha's protection be with you", which is the spirit of a mantra, then it is a splendid "mantra practice." It is not only a bestowing of the Truth on the other party but also a gift of Truth to oneself. Even in conversation, use only words that brighten both oneself and others. It is said that during a difficult trial the judge addressed the accused with a gentle term. This one gentle word so touched the accused's heart that, with tears in his eyes, he confessed everything. To read good books is also mantra practice. When you read a good book, its spirit becomes a part of you. In this sense, there is no greater gift than to present good books to others.

The uniqueness of the mantra practice is that since it is centered on "words," it is highly transmittable. For one's mantra practice to change into love practice is a joy. This is exactly the same as the sense in which "adornment of the divine image" is directly connected with love practice. Using good words is a way of bringing to fulfilment the complementary relationship of making oneself bright and cheery and making others feel the same.

*The Mantra in the way of good health.*   Mantra practice is not only a way of building up the mind but also of building up the body. To recite means to take deep breaths and vocalize strongly, and this in itself is directly linked to health. Melodious recitation requires strength in the *tanden* and long, strong exhalation. These are two indispensable conditions of the way of good health. Many people find that their health improves after they take voice lessons. This too is part of the purpose of sutra reciting and incantations. Consequently, people who really participate in sutra reciting and incantation must make an effort to straighten their posture, hold high their clasped hands, tuck in the chin, and place power in the *tanden*. The inhaled breath must of course also be strong and deep, and vocalization must be bold, long, and smooth. Sutra chanting provides wondrous benefits as a way toward good health, so the mantra way, with its principle of multiplication evident in the mutually beneficial effects of body and mind, should increasingly demonstrate its value.

## PURIFICATION

*Meaning of the word "effort."*   In the foregoing consideration of the divine image and mantra, the mind was in the forefront and the body in the background, but as we turn to purification and meditation, the body comes to the fore and the mind plays the minor role.

"Purification," which here refers to bodily purification, means the health way in our daily lives and has long been characterized by the word "assiduity." It might not improperly be called an "assiduity way," but the risk is that many would then interpret it simply as "effort." I venture to call it, therefore, a way of bodily purification. In the "Eightfold Noble Path" and the "Six Precepts for Deliverance," Buddha does mention "assiduousness,' but what he has reference to is not simply "effort." "Assiduousness" points precisely to the practice of the way of good health. For a long time, most Buddhist scholars misconstrued the meaning of this term, but strangely enough, ordinary people knew exactly what it meant. This is proof that the influence of outstanding Buddhist leaders from times past still lives on today.

Athletes undergo strenuous practice on the field. If they are great athletes, their efforts are not limited to the practice sessions. This great effort always is carried over into their daily lives. They must be diligent in carrying out a strict regimen that covers every aspect of their lives, including such things as cold baths, exercises, getting to bed early and getting up early. If they led slovenly lives, all their practice on the field would be useless.

Meditation is, then, like the effort of an athlete on the field, while "assiduity" resembles the effort the athlete makes in his daily life. One cannot say which of these two is the more important. To attain the goal, both must be practiced. It is also to be emphasized that meditation and assiduity form an inseparable yin-yang pair.

Long ago, when I was an apprentice priest, I was often sent on errands to a neighboring Zen temple. Morning or evening, the priest always smelled of liquor. He loved to tease me by offering me his "tea of wisdom." This priest had a stroke when he was only a little over fifty years of age and died without being able to engage in his final meditation. How meaningless is meditation without assiduousness!

We Buddhists have what we call "assiduity cooking," and it is common knowledge now that this is a way of cooking that entails abstaining from fish and meat. But its true value does not seem to be fully understood. Abstinence from animal food is directly connected with nonkilling and puts into practice the teaching of Buddha to esteem all living things. But Buddha did not necessarily prohibit the eating of meat and fish. Whenever a priest received an offering of food in his begging bowl, it was understood that he would accept it gratefully even if it contained meat or fish. As long as the animal was not killed especially for him, it was permissible. Thus Buddha is said to have eaten animal food too. But since many people observed the precept against killing, their chances of eating meat were no doubt extremely rare.

To abstain from animal food for the sake of the practice of love was the spirit that animated Buddha, but another important reason for this abstention was to maintain health. Buddha set forth many precepts regarding food, but he seems to have emphasized food precepts more for the sake of health than for the sake of love. He drew attention to many points that concerned not only food but all phases of life involving health. That his teaching had this outcome is only natural after his six years of profound Yoga experience. But today's Buddhists seem for the most part to have forgotten this spirit. Buddhism, which should be a "way of body and mind," has fallen into a one-sided "way of the mind."

*Buddhism invariably a way of body and mind.*   The way of good health emphasized by Buddha is not merely an "expedient way" to attain enlightenment. Just as it is wrong to say "enlightenment for the sake of health," so is it wrong to say "health for the sake of enlightenment." In the case of a couple, a woman is not a woman for the sake of the man, nor is the man a man for the sake of the woman. Neither is an object or a means. If by some mistaken notion, one mate should be used as a means, a family hell would result. Again, in the case of mind and body, neither is an object or an instrument. To deviate from this is to deviate from Buddha's Buddhism. Man's body and mind are united like a husband and wife. This was discovered by Yoga and brought to completion by Buddha. Indeed, where there is no correct physical health, there can be no correct mental health. To put it simply, enlightenment is but the working of the brain. Depending on how the brain's formation changes, one's thoughts will change. And the brain is but a part of the body. When the body undergoes a change, the brain cannot help but change. When I was young, I believed that even if the body got drunk, the mind would stay sober. One night after having wined and dined at a member's home, I started to drive back along Seattle's coastal drive. The ocean was on the right-hand side of the highway, so going off the road could have meant curtains. But no matter how I tried, the car kept straying to the right. That night I learned by experience how false it is to say, "Even if the body is intoxicated, the mind will stay sober." Finally, I stopped by the side of the road and took a brief nap. Since then, I have followed Buddha's precept not to become intoxicated.

Again, when the mind is not right, correct health cannot exist. Though you may say you are going to make yourself healthy, it is the mind that has to make this decision, so if the mind is headed in another direction, the way of good health will lose all meaning. This can be understood from the fact that even among Buddhist disciples, there are many with poor health even though Buddhism itself is so imbued with the health way. Physical health thus begins with the mind, but at the same time the mind is determined by the health condition of the physical brain, so again a healthy mind begins with a healthy body. There is no end to this kind of interrelation. It may be called a "circular principle."

*Entreaty to Buddhist organizations.* Styles of living today differ greatly from those of Buddha's era. Buddha's precepts and health way were meant for the mode of life of his day, so some of his precepts are unnecessary today. Take for example, the precept "Partake of food only in the morning, not in the afternoon." In those days there was no electricity, so I imagine people went to bed much earlier than now. Buddha, who perceived that intestinal stasis was one of the greatest enemies of health and truth-seeking, naturally taught this precept with this in mind, but conditions are much different today. To practice rigidly the precepts of Buddha without taking this changed state into consideration does not necessarily mean you are a faithful Buddhist disciple. To practice a health way suitable to today's mode of living, however, is to be a true practitioner of the precepts and a truth-seeker. This means that the words of the precepts need to be revised.

I frequently caution people not to eat canned foods. Of course, Buddha never said such a thing, but knowing that canned foods are a cause of intestinal stasis, I am just following the spirit of Buddha's teaching. Accordingly, in my discussion of the way of good health, I have ventured to give warnings about matters Buddha himself did not mention.

In this sense, there are two important changes I wish to recommend for today's Buddhist temples. One is to provide a fasting dormitory, and the other, to provide a water practice hall. These two are not easy to practice at home. The fasting dormitory should be so equipped that fasters can live there for the entire period of their fast. It would be perfect if the water practice hall were equipped with a strong water-jet facility and a hot-cold bath area.

To help people of today who have been exposed to devitalized, unnatural foods, fasting is the best method. Even in the olden days when food was natural, fasting was an indispensable course for truth-seekers. Even Buddha was able to become Buddha only by virtue of repeated fasting. How much more so in this age of unwholesome food inundation! Fasting has become many times more necessary than in the past. When you fast, the blood becomes purified, the brain becomes sharp, the personality improves, and you become able to eliminate most diseases. To the ladies, I will add that the skin also becomes beautiful.

Buddha has cautioned against "extreme asceticism" because it breaks down health and damages the brain. He always encouraged what would improve the health and brain. In this sense, suitable fasting is a marvelous method. But there are many difficulties when one tries to do it at home, so I hope the temples will help make fasting possible for the people.

There is nothing that gives such instantaneous improvement to blood circulation as the water practice. Buddha too was a water practitioner, and in Japan the very word "practitioner" instantly brings to mind a man standing under a waterfall. This is also difficult to practice at home, so I hope the temples will provide the opportunity. Try practicing meditation right after water practice. The effect will be several times greater than meditation alone. I would stake my life on it that fasting and water practice should be encouraged for all. Do not imagine them to be rigorous practices. I do not encourage extremes, because they destroy the brain and health. The "effort" I speak of is meant to benefit the brain and health. There is no other way for man to attain happiness.

## ZEN MEDITATION

*Meditation and the removal of stiffness.*  When asked, "What is the purpose of meditation?" my answer is always, "It is a way to take away the stiffness of body and mind." I think there is no way to express more simply the meaning of "meditation."

The cause of any kind of "physical disorder," any form of "mental abnormality," can be concisely explained in the one word "stiffness." So in case of sickness or worry, first think of getting rid of the "stiffness." This was the reason for the development of my "Eightfold unified way." When the supply of oxygen is inadequate, no matter how well one eats, the nutritive value cannot be burned completely. This causes the blood to become sticky and the nerves to become unbalanced, with the result that blood circulation becomes sluggish. Therefore, a breathing method was established. Without correct nutrition, the bones, flesh, and nerves cannot be renewed, so they become aged and harden. That is why a diet method was established. When the skin weakens, excretion of toxins become inadequate and causes autotoxis which in turn causes blood clotting. Consequently, a skin care way was set up. Unless exercises are done correctly, opportunity to rectify dislocation of the joints is lost and rigid muscles cannot be loosened. Therefore a body alignment method was set up. Thus these "four conditions for the way of good health" were established to take away all "physical stiffness" and regulate blood circulation from all angles.

When the sense of freedom is lacking, a state of mental suffocation arises and causes mental rigidity. This called for the establishment of the way of deliverance. When the joy of creating is lacking, the mind becomes dark from disappointment, so a mind-only method was set up. When the practice of love is not satisfactory, the mind is seized by a feeling of loneliness and shrinks in on itself, so the way of the practice of love was established. When self-training is not complete, the self cannot be settled and is disturbed by changing circumstances, so the way of self-training was established. Thus these "four conditions for enlightenment" were established to ascertain the causes of mental rigidity and secure the free, unhindered mind.

The "Eightfold unified way" can be further dissected and divided into countless laws. But no matter how minute or detailed it becomes, in all its aspects it always comes down to simple release from stiffness. Consequently, whether this method is to be adjudged superior or inferior can be decided by how effective it is in removing stiffness.

Why is it that man likes beautiful pictures and music? It is because they melt away the stiffness of the mind. The value of a picture or piece of music can be determined by how much stiffness they have the power to remove. This is the context in which the absolute value of "meditation" is established.

*The acme of practice of the way of body and mind in reliance on the multiplication principle.* Meditation begins with the adjustment of posture and breathing. As a result of adjusting the posture, blood circulation improves. In consequence of regulating the breath, the blood is purified. When blood circulation and blood quality improve simultaneously, the multiplication principle goes into action and washes away the stiffness of the body.

The effectiveness of the combined power of proper breathing and meditation posture can be glimpsed by the use of a sphygmomanometer. People with a tendency toward high blood pressure will immediately see a decline of 5 or 10 degrees, proof that rigidity has been removed from the blood vessels. Irregular heart beat will become regular and peaceful without fail. For cancer no fast proof of improvement is possible, but if meditation is practiced twenty minutes daily for several weeks, an improvement can be seen.

After adjusting posture and breathing, we need to turn next to "mind adjustment." "Mind adjustment" is to regulate the feeling of freedom and love. Forgetting my true self, which is by nature free and unhindered, am I being carried away by desolate thoughts? Has the true aspect that I love all and everyone loves me been forgotten? To the degree that one's feeling of freedom and love is corrected, stiffness of the mind is removed. Worry, anger, contempt, arrogance, greed, hate—all these are sources of mental rigidity. When they start to permeate your mind, the mind loses its freedom and your face becomes gloomy. The degree to which stiffness of the mind has been removed can be determined to some extent by testing one's brain waves or blood, but the simplest test is to measure the breathing.

A change in man's mental state is always reflected in his breathing. Mind and breath are directly connected, so when the breathing becomes irregular, the mind becomes restless, and when the mind is agitated, the breath becomes irregular. "Breath is a barometer of the mind." A deep, peaceful sleep is an indication of deep and good breathing, and more than anything else, good breathing is a manifestation of a "serene mind."

Meditation is like a deep sleep except that instead of lying down, you are sitting up. That is the only difference.

Meditation involves one multiplication principle as between posture and breath, another as between the feelings of freedom and love, and a third constituted by the combination of these two multiplication principles. Meditation takes away the stiffness of the mind at the same time it takes away the stiffness of the body. The mind and body mutually eradicate each other's stiffness and build up a flawless "mind and body without stiffness." That is precisely what it means to be a buddha—to be released from all restraints to enter a state of unhindered freedom and to manifest the highest joy and exercise of one's capabilities.

Nothing conforms more closely to body and mind as related by the multiplication principle than meditation. That is the reason it develops the supreme state of unhindered freedom. It is no exaggeration to say that all one's self-training throughout life is but a preparation for better meditation. For all life's affairs are but a quest for the sense of unhindered freedom which meditation makes it possible to realize at the highest level. That is why Buddha placed "meditation" at the very end of his Eightfold Noble Path.

*How to meditate.*   The first step in meditation is to take the "praying hands" position and bow in respect to the seat where you are going to sit. Regard it as a seat where Buddha himself once sat. A cushion may be placed on the seat or mat at your option. Sit in a lotus position, a half lotus position, in Japanese style, or on a chair, as you please. The best way is to train yourself to be able to do it in any position according to your condition and the time and place.

The body frame and muscles should be adjusted before meditation, but when you are not prepared, do the following sitting exercises. Countless sitting exercises were developed within Chinese Yoga. The uniqueness of these exercises is that body alignment can be achieved easily while sitting.

1.   Neck rotation. Relax neck and drop head forward. Rotate clockwise three times, counterclockwise three times, slowly like the hands of a clock.

2.   Shoulder relaxation. Bend arms and lift elbows up sideways to shoulder height, horizontal to floor and push back, drawing shoulder blades together. Chin juts out and upward. Repeat three times.

3.   Torso twist. Twist the spine as much as possible. Place both hands on the outside of right thigh, push and twist torso to right. Try to see your back. Reverse. Repeat three times.

4.   Hip bending. Place hands on thighs, keeping spinal column straight, bending from the hips. Lean forward and back, three times each. To the right front and left back, three times each. Left front and right back, three times each. Right and left three times each. When body is inclined, put power into the *tanden*. When body is erect, release the power.

5.   Abdomen squeeze. Place both hands on the *tanden*. Bend body forward while exhaling, and pull in abdomen as if you were squeezing the blood out of the *tanden*. Repeat three times.

On position of the palms, many mudras have been developed in Buddhism. This is a method whereby the mind is shaped according to the shape in which the palms are held. In this method stiffness of body and mind are effectively removed through putting the arms, palms, and fingers into various positions. Of the numerous mudras, I will explain two that are representative. To make the body pliant, place your hands in your lap, palms up, letting the tips of the thumb and index finger of each hand touch to form the letter "O." To make the mind pliant, place both hands in the lap, palms up with the right palm on top of the left; again let the tips of the thumbs and index fingers form the letter "O," and draw the little-finger side of the hands into the lower abdomen. The sense of contact between thumb and index finger improves the breathing. This feeling of contact also accelerates the multiplication principles at work in body and mind, posture and breathing, freedom and love.

The points to remember for correct posture are: draw back the chin and pubic bone, pull up the head and chest, and relax the neck and shoulders. The shoulders should be horizontal and one shoulder should not be ahead or behind the other. Keep the nose and navel on the same perpendicular line.

Keep your eyes half open. Decide on a point one to three yards in front of you, and once your eyes are riveted on the point, do not let your eyes wander. Try not to blink.

As for breathing, in the beginning do the following "training breathing" about ten times. Inhale deeply, hold your breath, and with abdominal pressure exhale strongly. The key to exhaling is to squeeze the rectum tightly. During inhalation, imagine that fresh air is entering from the top of your head, proceeding down the spine, and entering your lower abdomen. When exhaling, imagine that the energy of the *tanden* is moving up the spine and emerging from the top of the head. After repeating the training breathing about ten times, continue steadfastly with long, smooth breathing. The breathing will become so quiet one cannot detect when an inhalation ends and an exhalation begins.

So much for the physical aspect of meditation. We turn next to the mental. Repeat inwardly some such words as the following:

"I now perceive that no phenomena in the universe really exist. I discern that I have neither body nor mind. There is no sin or evil in this world. I see in this moment my true self, a self overflowing with unlimited freedom and love. From the eternal past to this very day, I have been a buddha, radiating infinite life and light. I perceive that all the gods and saints who have ever appeared in this universe are identical with myself. I see that I love all from the bottom of my heart, and that all love me as well. Infinite freedom and love, infinite freedom and love, infinite freedom and love . . ."

Here, recite any mantra you find suitable. The recitation will gradually grow fainter, and the fainter it gets, the higher the state of unhindered freedom you attain. The recitation will naturally fade away and the mind lose all awareness. The body becomes infinitely clear, the mind infinitely transparent. Perfect cooperation between mind and body is attained, and the original self emerges. This is the embodiment of the most sublime beauty life possesses. This is indeed meditation. Meditation must be practiced at least twenty minutes a day in order to get results. It can be divided into two sessions of ten minutes each, one in the morning and one at night. Take a picture of yourself before you start meditation, and another picture, in the same pose, two months later. Show it to others, and they will tell you, after only a glance, that you have changed for the better.

# Conclusion

The appended "Diagram of the Thirty-two Principles of the Way of Body and Mind" was constructed in the desire to make it easier to understand and practice this way. Each of the thirty-two principles is founded on the yin-yang principle, and together they form a harmonious oneness. Not one may be omitted if a man would be wholly saved.

All diseases can be traced to a single cause—impure blood. As soon as the impurity is removed, the illness disappears. What causes the impurity? There are always two sources. One is the bad quality of the blood, and the other is poor blood circulation. When these two return to normal, the blood becomes pure, and when the blood becomes pure, sickness is washed away. This is the key to curing sickness. To improve blood quality, breathing and diet must be corrected, and to stimulate blood circulation, skin and bone structure must be corrected. Breath, food, skin, and exercise are the components of the way of the body.

All life's worries can be traced to a single cause—impurity of the mind. As soon as this impurity is removed, troubles disappear. What causes this impurity? There are always two sources: bad quality of the mind and poor mind circulation. When these two return to normal, the mind becomes pure, and when the mind is pure, fears and worries are washed away. This is the key to resolving mental distress. To improve the quality of the mind, one must learn that "man is by nature a god possessing unlimited freedom and love," and that "all my happiness and unhappiness is the result of my subconscious mind, so I must concentrate on purifying my subconscious mind." Again to, improve mind circulation, the practice of love and self-training must be undertaken. Awakening, mind, the practice of love, and self-training are the components of the way of the mind.

"Blood quality and blood circulation," "mind quality and mind circulation" —some of these are unheard of expressions, but unless expressed in this way, the cause of disease and mental distress cannot be correctly probed. This is why I have ventured to coin new expressions. When you become sick, think, "How is my blood quality and circulation?" When problems arise, reflect, "How is my mind quality and circulation?"

Furthermore, "mind impurity" will soon bring about "impure blood", and "impure blood" will directly invite "impure mind." If you harbor discontent and forget to feel appreciative, the blood immediately becomes acidified, toxic, and cloudy. And when the body starts to lack sufficient oxygen and calcium the mind becomes irritable, loses harmony, and falls prey to insomnia. When disintegration occurs in any one of the four components of the way of the mind, the body becomes sick, and when a defect occurs in any one of the four components of the way of the body, the mind feels stress. Impurity of the mind and impurity of the blood are exactly the same thing, and purifying the mind and purifying the blood are also identical.

Body and mind are like the two wings of a bird—one is useless without the other. The way worked out in consequence of grasping this truth is Buddhist Yoga. Whether regarded as a religion or a way of health, it is a path thoroughly dedicated to man.

DIAGRAM OF THE THIRTY-TWO PRINCIPLES OF THE WAY OF BODY AND MIND (EIGHTFOLD UNIFIED WAY)

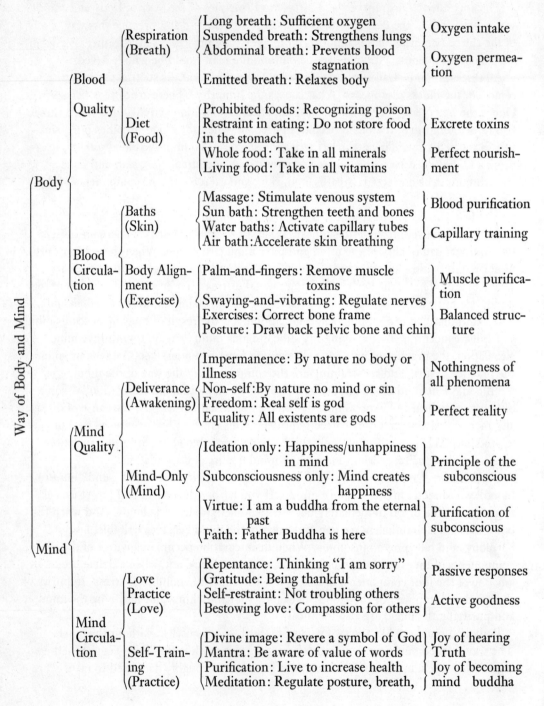

Way of Body and Mind

Body
- Blood Quality
  - Respiration (Breath)
    - Long breath: Sufficient oxygen — } Oxygen intake
    - Suspended breath: Strengthens lungs
    - Abdominal breath: Prevents blood stagnation — } Oxygen permeation
    - Emitted breath: Relaxes body
  - Diet (Food)
    - Prohibited foods: Recognizing poison — } Excrete toxins
    - Restraint in eating: Do not store food in the stomach
    - Whole food: Take in all minerals — } Perfect nourishment
    - Living food: Take in all vitamins
- Blood Circulation
  - Baths (Skin)
    - Massage: Stimulate venous system — } Blood purification
    - Sun bath: Strengthen teeth and bones
    - Water baths: Activate capillary tubes — } Capillary training
    - Air bath: Accelerate skin breathing
  - Body Alignment (Exercise)
    - Palm-and-fingers: Remove muscle toxins — } Muscle purification
    - Swaying-and-vibrating: Regulate nerves
    - Exercises: Correct bone frame — } Balanced structure
    - Posture: Draw back pelvic bone and chin

Mind
- Mind Quality
  - Deliverance (Awakening)
    - Impermanence: By nature no body or illness — } Nothingness of all phenomena
    - Non-self: By nature no mind or sin
    - Freedom: Real self is god — } Perfect reality
    - Equality: All existents are gods
  - Mind-Only (Mind)
    - Ideation only: Happiness/unhappiness in mind — } Principle of the subconscious
    - Subconsciousness only: Mind creates happiness
    - Virtue: I am a buddha from the eternal past — } Purification of subconscious
    - Faith: Father Buddha is here
- Mind Circulation
  - Love Practice (Love)
    - Repentance: Thinking "I am sorry" — } Passive responses
    - Gratitude: Being thankful
    - Self-restraint: Not troubling others — } Active goodness
    - Bestowing love: Compassion for others
  - Self-Training (Practice)
    - Divine image: Revere a symbol of God — Joy of hearing Truth
    - Mantra: Be aware of value of words
    - Purification: Live to increase health — Joy of becoming mind buddha
    - Meditation: Regulate posture, breath,

## Buddhahood through Utilization of the Seven Points Where the Multiplication Principle Appears in the Way of Body and Mind

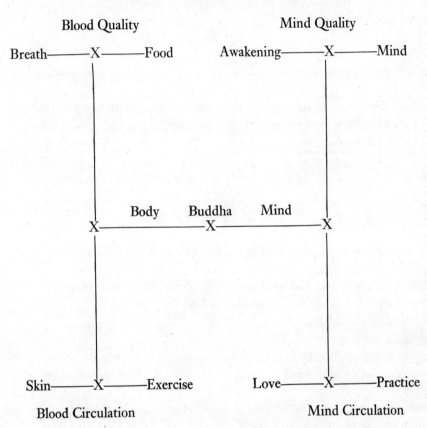

Blood Quality

Breath———X———Food

Mind Quality

Awakening———X———Mind

Body    Buddha    Mind

X————————X————————X

Skin———X———Exercise

Blood Circulation

Love———X———Practice

Mind Circulation

# CREED OF THE DHARMA YOGA CHURCH

1.   The only light for human life is truth and one's self. Therefore, I will never rest in my efforts to understand the truth and to train myself.

2.   Man is an entity of oneness of mind and body which is based on the multiplication theory. Therefore, I shall develop my cheerfulness and health equally.

3.   All religions and health methods are manifestations of the fervent desire of One Universal Life. Therefore, I shall unite all their good points and walk the great way of ultimate, perfect completion.

4.   The three conditions of time, place and man are always changing. Therefore, I shall freely use any suitable expedience in order to accomplish my love practice.

5.   The establishment of world peace depends on the practice of Dharma Yoga. Therefore, I shall treasure the harmony of our precious Sangha and spread the way of Dharma Yoga to all mankind.

In the presence of the One Universal God, I vow to uphold this creed.

## THOUGHT OF ZEN

My true self has, no sickness and death, but infinite health and eternal Life.

My true self has, no sin and hindrance, but infinite light and omnipotent Life.
My true self is, an original child of God, a Buddha.
Body Buddha—Mind Buddha
My Buddha—Everyone's Buddha
Constant Buddha—Father Buddha
I am a precious child of God. I repent that I have despised myself, since the beginningless past.
Everyone is a precious child of God. I repent that I have despised others, since the beginningless past.
The pouring of Father Buddha, ceaseless rain of Light,
    Thankful am I, Thankful am I.
       "Nam Cheerful Thankful Mind"
         Amen
           "Nam Cheerful Thankful Mind"
             Amen